MOLECULAR PSYCHOBIOLOGY

A Chemical Approach to Learning and
Other Behavior

Publication Number 661
AMERICAN LECTURE SERIES®

A Monograph in
The BANNERSTONE DIVISION *of*
AMERICAN LECTURES IN LIVING CHEMISTRY

Edited by
I. NEWTON KUGELMASS, M.D., Ph.D., Sc.D.
Consultant to the Departments of Health and Hospital
New York, New York

MOLECULAR PSYCHOBIOLOGY

A Chemical Approach to Learning and Other Behavior

By

JOHN GAITO, Ph.D.

Director, Molecular Psychobiology Laboratory
York University
Toronto, Ontario, Canada

CHARLES C THOMAS · PUBLISHER
Springfield · Illinois · U.S.A.

Published and Distributed Throughout the World by
CHARLES C THOMAS • PUBLISHER
BANNERSTONE HOUSE
301-327 East Lawrence Avenue, Springfield, Illinois, U.S.A.
NATCHEZ PLANTATION HOUSE
735 North Atlantic Boulevard, Fort Lauderdale, Florida, U.S.A.

© *1966, by* CHARLES C THOMAS • PUBLISHER
Library of Congress Catalog Card Number: 66-18929

*With THOMAS BOOKS careful attention is given to all details of
manufacturing and design. It is the Publisher's desire to present
books that are satisfactory as to their physical qualities and artistic
possibilities and appropriate for their particular use. THOMAS
BOOKS will be true to those laws of quality that assure a good
name and good will.*

Printed in the United States of America
N-1

**To Olly, DAN,
Steve, and DoNnA**

FOREWORD

OUR LIVING CHEMISTRY SERIES was conceived by Editor and Publisher to advance the newer knowledge of chemical medicine in the cause of clinical practice. The interdependence of chemistry and medicine is so great that physicians are turning to chemistry, and chemists to medicine in order to understand the underlying basis of life processes in health and disease. Once chemical truths, proofs and convictions become sound foundations for clinical phenomena, key hybrid investigators clarify the bewildering panorama of biochemical progress for application in everyday practice, stimulation of experimental research and extension of postgraduate instruction. Each of our monographs thus unravels the chemical mechanisms and clinical management of many diseases that have remained relatively static in the minds of medical men for three thousand years. Our new Series is charged with the *nisus élan* of chemical wisdom, supreme in choice of international authors, optimal in standards of chemical scholarship, provocative in imagination for experimental research, comprehensive in discussions of scientific medicine and authoritative in chemical perspective of human disorders.

Dr. Gaito of Toronto integrates the current concepts of psychology with the revolutionary achievements in molecular biology to create the new discipline — molecular psychobiology in both mechanism and methodology. Molecular biology was applied originally to studies of proteins and nucleic acids to unravel the molecular nature of gene structure, replication and expression, but was extended to molecular psychobiology to explain biological phenomena of the mind in terms of three-dimensional molecules with the aid of powerful new experimental techniques. It is natural for us to think in terms of molecules now since they are our tools of investigation and means of expression or symbols of our understanding of the physicochemical process of life. And it is far more stimulating to the imagination than the myth of two centuries ago that the brain was a concoction of spirits which might be pure and tranquil, or riotous and evil. The gradual discovery that the central nervous system consists of an immense universe of highly complex units has influenced man's conception of himself, and the method of training the extraordinary organization of neurons with which he is endowed. *Ancora imparo.*

We are taught to be self-reliant, and enterprising in the details of life, but dependent, unreflective, *laissez-faire* about life itself. The idea that the basis of living could be really and radically altered is outside most people's orbit, but the author's revelations reinterpret living phenomena in terms of the molecular basis of memory, learning and behavior clarifying mental mechanisms from the protein structure and metabolism of the brain; interpreting psychometabolism with the raw materials of subjective experience transformed into psycho-socially operative organizations of thought and feeling; revealing the interaction of the various parts of the brain which generates the highest of all functions that express themselves in psychic phenomena, as conscience, memory, recall and learning; correlating brain development with learning under genotypic control; analyzing current problems in behavior yet "wearing all that weight of learning lightly like a flower." The views of Cajal and Sherrington, of Titchener and Watson, of Koffka and Meyer, of Pavlov and Freud — often considered rival conceptions — merge into molecular psychobiology complementary to each other. Mind is the great lever of all things and human thought, the process by which human ends are ultimately answered.

The core of molecular biology is embodied in the well known aphorism: DNA $\longrightarrow$ m RNA $\longrightarrow$ protein, the arrows implying the transfer of information. The structure of DNA molecules in the nucleus of egg and sperm is the information code of the gene which informs each oncoming generation how to make a person. As a template it synthesizes RNA to produce the cell's proteins. Modifications of neuronal RNA, the basis of information storage in the brain for DNA and RNA with their highly specific code of arrangements of patterns of four-linked bases, constitute

the blueprint for heredity. Memory traces are established by reverberating electrical circuits in patterns of action of many
neurons in the early stages of recording information. But permanent storage of the memory trace is affected by enduring chemical
changes in the submicroscopic compartments of neurons. Circulation of impulses precedes establishment of memory and recurs to
reproduce the sensations caused by the original experience.
Certain drugs facilitate storage of acquired information and the
learning process. Neuronal RNA increases markedly during impulse conduction accompanied by enhanced protein synthesis
which represents the memory traces. Statistically, RNA and protein molecules furnish the necessary permutation possibilities to
store the memory experience of a lifetime.

The development and propagation of permanently wired-in
computer-control networks account for the inherited pattern of
behavior essential for survival with a library of specifications transmitted by the genes in coded form from one generation to the
next. As more is known about the physical and chemical laws by
means of which the structural pattern of a gene controls the mole-
cule-binding processes in the surrounding protoplasm, more detailed translation of the messages conveyed by the genes of an
individual will be worked out. Genotypically, man bears a particular molecular sequence of carbon, hydrogen, oxygen, nitrogen and
phosphorus atoms — the length of DNA tightly coiled in the
nucleus of the provenient egg and in the nucleus of every adult
cell, five thousand million paired nucleotide units long, a store of
information that specifies ten million kinds of proteins. The
lottery of gene inheritance assures man of his biochemical, physiological and psychological individuality. Molecular biology thus
demonstrates the uselessness of the old dichotomy of heredity and
environment in the life of each cell, for each reaction in a
sequence of reactions is dependent on the product of previous
interaction of the genic patterning and its environment.

The dust is not beginning to settle in the greatest upheavel in
biological sciences, with foundations laid for a hybrid science, in
the successful inquiry into vital questions that seemed far beyond
the reach of classical biology a decade ago. *Dimidium facti qui*

coepit labet. The ambiguous language of behavioral science is attaining greater precision borrowing strength from multiple disciplines valuable to the psychologist interested in human behavior genetics, the geneticist concerned with recent psychological ideas and methods, and the physician geared for possible applications to clinical problems. The thesis stirs interest in the science of learning and behavior encouraging the attitude of the motto of the oldest scientific society: *Nullins in verbs.* It gives us a picture of a functioning entity which obviates resort to what Isaac Newton called "occult qualities of the mind" but his great ocean of truth remains all undiscovered before us. The future psychobiologist will thus require the unusual faculty of perceiving life in unhabitual ways and transcend Aristotelian logic with the breadth of vision of a Socrates, the mathematical capacity of a La Place, the chemical ingenuity of an Arrhenius, the humanitarian interest of a Leonardo da Vinci and the abstract expression of an Einstein.

> *"Speak, ye, the pure delight, whose favoured steps*
> *The lamp of science thro' the jealous maze*
> *Of nature guides, when haply you reveal*
> *Her secret honours."*

I. NEWTON KUGELMASS, M.D., Ph.D., Sc.D., *Editor*

PREFACE

T HE RECENT EXCITEMENT and rapid advances in molecular biology have greatly influenced the thinking of many behavioral scientists. The molecular biological ideas and techniques which could be relevant to the molecular aspects of behavior are scattered widely throughout the literature, however, being mainly in sources which many behavioral scientists may not read and are too technical for many to fully comprehend. Likewise, many molecular biologists are not familiar with important behavioral information. Thus there exists a need for a book to bridge the gap between molecular biology and behavioral science, a book written in a simplified fashion for sophisticated scientists as well as for students. This effort hopes to attain that purpose; it is for a broad audience — from molecular biologists to psychologists and from the sophisticated to the naive.

The orientation throughout the book is a molecular biological one. The complex behavior which the psychologist or psychiatrist, or other behavioral scientists, are concerned with has its foundations in intra- and intercellular events which rely on gene and gene product interactions. The attitude is taken that a fruitful approach to understanding behavior is that of extending the ideas and techniques which have been so successful with viruses and bacteria to the study of higher organisms.

Thus the domain of molecular psychobiology could be a common ground for psychiatrists and other medical men, psychologists, biochemists, biophysicists, virologists, bacteriologists, geneticists, cytologists, neurophysiologists, neurochemists and neurohistologists.

ACKNOWLEDGMENTS

T HESE MATERIALS ARE the culmination of the work of a number of years. I have been influenced in my thinking by interaction with colleagues and students (graduate and undergraduate) in biological and behavioral sciences. These individuals are too numerous to mention. I have been influenced especially by Abraham Eisenstark and Richard Consigli of the Microbial Genetics and Virology Laboratory at Kansas State University, who allowed me to work in their laboratory and guided me through the difficult task of learning molecular biological procedures.

A number of individuals were kind enough to read a preliminary draft, or portions of it. I am especially grateful to Ernest Barrett, Charles Snowdon, Abraham Eisenstark, Ralph Gerard and Mary Telfer for their helpful comments. I want to acknowledge also that James Bonner, Abraham Eisenstark, and Richard Consigli contributed valuable comments for the suggested research programs discussed in various portions of this book.

I am grateful to Margery Adamson for typing the preliminary draft and portions of the later one; to Carolyn Aurich, Donna Hughes and Joan Hancock for typing the revised manuscript; and to Dan Gaito for assistance in the drawing of the various figures scattered throughout the book.

My research reported in Chapters 8 and 10 was supported by the Faculty Research Fund of Kansas State University and by the National Research Council of Canada.

J. G.

CONTENTS

Contents

MOLECULAR PSYCHOBIOLOGY

**A Chemical Approach to Learning and
Other Behavior**

SECTION I
GENERAL ASPECTS AND DESCRIPTION

CHAPTER 1

INTRODUCTION

T HE WORK ON THE nucleic acids during recent years has been acclaimed by some individuals as resulting in the greatest biological discovery in the twentieth century. The advances in this area have been extremely rapid with researchers from multiple disciplines actively at work. For structural genes, the transfer of genetic information during protein synthesis which involves deoxyribonucleic acid (DNA), a number of ribonucleic acids (RNA) and amino acids has been well analyzed. Tentative RNA codes have been proposed for each amino acid. An air of excitement and enthusiasm seems to permeate researchers with the expectation that man is getting closer and closer to nature's basic secrets.

In that the linear sequence of bases in DNA provides the information which specifies the genetic potentialities of an organism, it was immediately evident to a number of behavioral scientists that the sequence of subunits in the nucleic acids or some other macromolecule might function directly or indirectly in experiential coding, i.e., maintain the information contained in memory. Thus the investigations concerned with the genetic coding have had a profound effect on a number of psychologists and other behavioral scientists who are concerned with complex behavior and have led to the development of an area which might be appropriately entitled *molecular psychobiology,* an integration of the ideas and methods of psychology and related behavioral sciences with those from molecular biology. This area includes some of the subject matter of biochemistry, physical chemistry, biophysics, virology, bacteriology, genetics, cytology, psychology, neurobiology, neurology, neurophysiology, neurochemistry and neurohistology.

This area of molecular psychobiology is a rapidly expanding one which should be of interest to many behavioral scientists in that it is concerned with some of the basic problems relative to behavior. Near at hand may be the possibility of determining the molecular basis for memory and the exact mechanisms involved in memory and other learning phenomena. A most exciting and welcome possibility!

The terminology of molecular psychobiology is probably strange to many behavioral scientists, e.g., concepts such as hydrogen bonding, hyperchromicity, nucleotides, nucleosides, bases, primary structure, secondary structure, tertiary structure, quaternary structure, enzymatic degradation, etc; various methods including nearest neighbor analysis, cesium chloride density gradient centrifugation, thermal denaturation, phenol extraction, ethanol precipitation, etc.; and apparatus such as high and low speed centrifuges, homogenizers and tissue grinders, spectrophotometers, dialyzers, lyophilizers, radiographic devices, etc. In the next decade this terminology should become more commonplace in behavioral science.

Although molecular psychobiology can be concerned with any molecular aspects underlying behavior, the emphasis has tended to be on the nucleic acids, DNA and RNA, a bias which this book will follow. It should be obvious, however, that the nucleic acids perform their function through the involvement of a sequence of biochemical events. It is difficult, if not impossible, to conduct experimental research with all aspects of a problem at one time. One must choose what he considers to be the most important or critical portion of the problem. Some individuals emphasize the DNA complex; others stress RNA events; and many suggest proteins, phospholipids, or other chemicals as the most basic aspects for behavior. Such a diversity of approach is healthy for science and should facilitate the convergence of experimental results to a common understanding of the neurochemical events during behavior.

Even though the main emphasis of molecular psychobiology is on molecular chemical aspects, information only at the molecular level would be fruitless. Thus this area of investigation must consider the determination of correlates on three levels, psychological, neurological and biochemical, for a more complete picture of behavior.

The molecular biological contributions which are most pertinent to molecular psychobiology are those concerned with heredity and the manner in which DNA performs its genetic function. The importance of molecular events in genetics and behavior can not be over-emphasized. For example, the difference between a normal individual and some anemics (sickle cell anemia) is due to *one* amino acid in hemoglobin. Such a small difference physically, but a great difference with regard to the resulting behavior! Likewise, slight modification in one amino acid in insulin may vitiate its function as an anti-diabetic agent. Numerous other examples could be cited.

As our understanding of these molecular events grows, it should be possible to alter human and lower organisms through chemical means. It is already possible to induce a permanent change in some viruses and bacteria which is passed on to later generations. It may be possible to create relatively harmless viruses which would crowd out disease producing ones and to manufacture a virus which would destroy cancerous cells but ignore healthy ones. At the human level, RNA therapy has been reported to improve the overall condition of elderly patients. The future for molecular biology and molecular psychobiology appears bright.

The important portions of this book are Sections II and III concerned with molecular biology and molecular psychobiology. However, to appreciate fully those topics relative to behavior, it is necessary to consider some preliminary material. The remaining pages of this section are devoted to nonmolecular topics.

CHAPTER 2

BEHAVIOR AND THE NERVOUS SYSTEM

GENERAL

IN DISCUSSING THE behavior of organisms, one usually begins with the paradigm:

Behavior = f (Heredity, Environmental Stimulation) or

Phenotype = f (Genotype, Environmental Stimulation), i.e., the expressed behavior depends on the interaction of genetic and environmental components.

The organism inherits certain potentials such as the potential for being a human being rather than a chimpanzee, the potential for blue eyes, the potential for certain intellectual abilities, the potential for emotional capacities, etc. Obviously the genetic mechanisms are important, to a greater or lesser degree, in all aspects of behavior. However, it is important to realize that the genetic contributions govern the developmental process and are only *potentials* which in some cases may not be actualized. The actualization of these potentials depend upon the second important component of behavioral determination, environmental stimulation (Dobzhansky, 1962).

There are two environmental aspects which influence the developing or actualizing of the genetic potential, an internal and an external one. The internal environment consists of those dynamic chemical events which permeate the organism. These events occur within the nucleus and cytoplasm of cells and in the interaction of cells with cells, tissues with tissues, and organs with organs, in the continuous process of biological integration. The external environmental influence involves the interaction of an organism with other organisms and with other aspects of his environment, and results in internal changes, the most important of which is some type of "memory traces" to symbolize or represent his life experiences.

Both of these environmental influences help to actualize, or block the actualization of, the potential which is specified by genetic material. For example, an individual may have the genetic potential for developing into a human organism with appropriate physical structure. However, as has occurred recently in a number of countries, if the mother has ingested thalidomide during the second or third month of pregnancy, the child may abort or be born without arms or legs, or with incomplete development of the limbs. Or if the newborn is deprived of oxygen supply for an undue length of time during the birth process (disrupting the delicate metabolic machinery of the cells), he can be born with paralytic and/or other deficiencies. Further, even the color of the eyes might be affected. The organism may have inherited the potential for brown eyes; however, if there is some disruption in the metabolic processes of the internal environment in which these potentials develop, he may have blue eyes instead. Or if some disruption occurs in the environment of only one eye, he may have one eye blue and the other brown.

The influence of the external environment on the actualization of genetic potentials is more subtle and difficult to indicate at the biochemical level. However, it is obviously there. Examples of this influence are the following. An individual may have inherited the potential for normal or greater intelligence, but if reared in a non-stimulating environment he may be relatively retarded in his intellectual development. The feral children illustrate this possibility as well as the canal-boat children of England and the backwoods people of certain communities in the United States. Many other examples can be invoked to indicate this point. The most important aspect of this influence is the learning process in which behavior is modified because of experiences and these experiences are recorded in the central nervous system in some way.

CELLS

Generalized Cell

The behavior of most animals is a complicated phenomenon which is difficult to understand because of the complexity of the brain which regulates it. To understand the function of the brain it is necessary to start with the basic unit of biological organisms, the cell. All tissues and organs of all animals consist of one or more cells specialized to perform certain functions. The prototype or general cell is shown in Figure 2-1 with the components which will be pertinent to this book.

The cell consists of two main parts, the nucleus and the cytoplasm. Each of these two has a membrane with pores, which is permeable to some substances but restricts others. In the nucleus of the cell are the chromosomes and genes, the latter being the basic units for heredity.

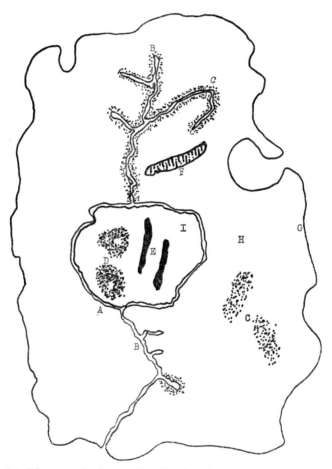

Figure 2-1. Diagram of a "generalized" cell with some components. A, nuclear membranes; B, endoplasmic reticulum; C, ribosomes; D, nucleoli; E, chromosomes; F, mitochondrion; G, cell membrane; H, cytoplasm; and I, nucleoplasm.

Communicating from the cell membrane to the nuclear membrane (in some cases) is the endoplasmic reticulum. Attached to the reticulum are ribosomes. The reticulum plus ribosomes are referred to as microsomes. The ribosomes also occur adhering to the cell membrane and unattached elsewhere in the cell. The ribosomes are important sites for the synthesis of protein. Cells in the pancreas and brain are particularly rich in microsomes. The nucleoli appear only at certain phases of cell function and are believed to be involved in RNA synthesis. The mitochondria are the "power plant" of the cell. Adenosine triphosphate (ATP) is synthesized and stored here for energy requirements.

In the process of evolution cells have specialized. The specialized cells relevant to behavior are: those concerned mainly with sensitivity (receptors); others, with sensitivity and conduction (nerve cells); others, with secretions (glands); and still others, with contractility (muscles). All of these are of importance in considering brain function. The most important cells for our purposes will be the nerve cells of the nervous system.

Nerve Cell

The nerve cell can take a number of forms; the one which is most common in brain tissue is a multipolar cell consisting of a number of dendrites, the soma or body of the cell and one axon (Figure 2-2). The constituents of nerve cells are the same as those in a generalized cell; however, the microsomes are called Nissl bodies. One exception to the similarity in contents of the two is that nerve cells contain gamma aminobutryic acid (GABA) whereas other cells do not. The possible significance of GABA will be discussed later.

The unique characteristic of nerve cells is their interconnection. The connections between the nerve cells in the nervous system are not continuous. Two or more nerve cells communicate functionally with one another through structural discontinuities which are the synapses. Figure 2-3 illustartes a synapse. A number of dendrites lead to the soma of the cell and one axon leads away from the soma. Impinging upon the soma or dendrites are a number of axons from other cells with an enlarged terminal ending. However, the cell membrane encases the ending, and thus there is no direct connection between the latter and the dendrite or soma upon which it impinges. Billions of cells tightly packed in the brain make for a tremendous number of synaptic junctions. Through electrical activity brain cells influence one another.

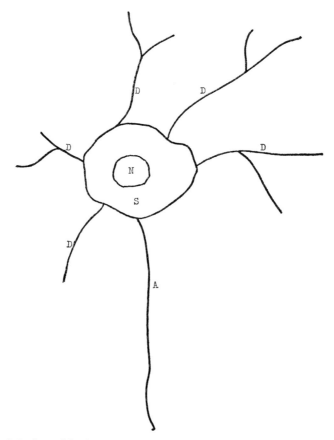

Figure 2-2. A multipolar nerve cell. D, dendrites; S, soma; N, nucleus; A, axon.

The electrical activity of nerve cells are of two types, nerve impulses and graded potentials. Nerve impulses involve transmission of information within a nerve cell by electrochemical events in the membrane. This event operates on an all-or-none basis, i.e., a nerve cell will be excited and initiate a nerve impulse if the exiting stimulus is intense enough; if the stimulus is of sub-threshold intensity no nerve impulse will be generated.

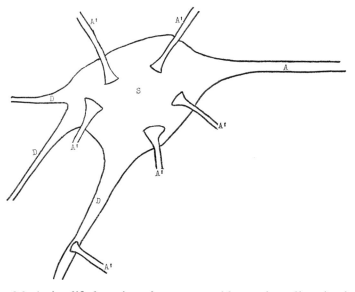

Figure 2-3. A simplified version of a synapse with axonic endings impinging on the soma and dendrites of a nerve cell. D, dendrites; S, soma; A, axon; A', axon from other nerve cells.

Tobias (1964) introduced an interesting set of hypotheses concerned with the manner in which an axon shifts from the resting to the excited state. The first step involved the movement of potassium from the cytoplasm of the axon into the membrane, which consists of lipid molecules sandwiched between protein molecules on the outside. This event brings about the displacement of calcium and an increase in the water content of the membrane. A loosening and spreading apart of membrane structural components occurs. This series of events is responsible for the reversible change in membrane structure which expresses itself as a fall in membrane resistance permitting the ion fluxes which accompany nerve impulses to supervene.

Kavanau (1965), in his membrane model, described the lipid-protein membrane as a dynamic and highly labile entity, shifting to different substructural states during different functional phases. The configuration of the lipid molecules changes most drastically during the functional states. During the "open" condition the pores are at their maximum size with the lipid molecules expanding from one side of the membrane to the other and absorbing much liquid. The membrane is at its maximum width. In the "closed" configuration the width of the membrane decreases; the pores are almost completely obliterated as the lipid molecules expand parallel to the protein sheaths of the membrane, and liquid is lost from the lipid phase. The "closed" state is a relatively stable one whereas the "open" configuration is very unstable. The protein sheaths are highly elastic, capable of rapid increases and decreases of surface area during these phases. In the axon the "closed" configuration corresponds to an unexcited fully recovered fiber; the "open" state, to the passage of the nerve impulse with the membrane becoming highly permeable to sodium ions.

The nerve impulse reaching the axonic ending results in a release of chemicals into the synaptic opening between the two cells. These chemicals increase or decrease the graded potential of the postsynaptic neuron, the second type of electrical activity of nerve cells. The graded potential appears to be related mainly to the dendrites and is an electrical potential varying in intensity irrespective of nerve impulse activity; it depends on the amount and type of the chemical released into the synaptic opening. When the graded potential reaches a certain level, a nerve impulse is initiated within the postsynaptic neuron. At the axonic ending, chemicals are released to affect the graded potential of the next neuron, and the cycle is repeated. The dendritic graded potentials of the many neurons in the brain are believed to induce field effects and influence the functioning of proximal and distal cells. The graded response or spreading electrical potential has been given an important role in learning by some individuals (Kohler and Held, 1949; Landauer, 1964). Morrell (1961) maintained that a growing body of knowledge suggests an important integrative function in the central nervous system for the graded response elements. The reaction of these elements varies with stimulus intensity, thus being different than membrane units which operate on an all-or-none basis to give a nerve impulse when stimulated by threshold intensities. Also, unlike nerve impulse units, a refractory period in which no stimulus is effective or a suprathreshold stimulus is required does not occur. This event allows these neural units to be continuously sensitive to stimulation.

Activation of dendrites is accompanied by more prolonged activity than is the case with activation of the soma (Gardner, 1963). This result makes it possible for successive impulses reaching the dendrite to maintain it in an active state so that more nerve impulses can be initiated than is the case of activation of the soma. Dendritic activity may be involved in facilitating the recurrences of nerve impulses over reverberatory circuits so as to maintain the effects of stimulation after the stimulus has been removed, a type of short term memory.

Although the graded potential appears to be mainly related to the dendrites, it has recently been recognized that graded responses take place, also, along the cell body and at the presynaptic terminals, and in glial cells (Pribram, 1963b).

Excitation across synaptic units appears to be of a chemical nature and is either excitatory or inhibitory (Eccles, 1959). Some neurons are excitatory; others are inhibitory. A given neuron may be excited by the direct action of an excitatory transmitter (synaptic excitation), by potentiated release of the transmitter from excitatory terminals (presynaptic excitation), or by inhibition of an inhibitory pathway (disinhibition). Inhibition of a neuron can occur by direct action of the inhibitory transmitter (synaptic inhibition) or through dampening the release of transmitter from excitatory terminals (presynaptic inhibition) (Salmoiraghi and Bloom, 1964).

A number of chemicals have been suggested as transmitter substances; acetylcholine (ACh) has been the favorite excitatory one. ACh is supposed to be released from presynaptic endings into the synapse and to depolarize the membrane of the postsynaptic neuron so that increased graded potentials occur (Fig. 2-4). If these potentials reach a threshold value, a nerve impulse is propagated. This definitely occurs in some autonomic synapses and it is assumed to occur also in central synapses. Salmoiraghi and

Bloom (1964) summarized a number of studies which showed that ACh had a functional cortical action: ACh administered by micropipettes increased the spontaneous discharge of many neurons; during ACh administration the cells were more easily discharged by visual or electrical stimulation; many of the responses to ACh were potentiated by Progstigmine, an inhibitor of acetylcholinesterase (AChE) which degrades ACh; some cortical motor neurons (Betz cells) are sensitive to ACh; and ACh is released from active cerebral tissue which also contains AChE. However, other excitatory transmitters are probably involved also (Ochs, 1965).

If another chemical of inhibitory nature (possibly GABA) is released into the synapse, chemical events occur in the post-synaptic membrane such that an increased threshold for excitation results, i.e., the graded potential is decreased. Killam (1958) suggested that GABA plays a role in establishing and maintaining normal patterned activity in the central nervous system, possibly affecting all synaptic transmission. GABA has been identified as a component of an inhibitory factor which is present in mammalian brain and which diminishes the discharge of impulses in

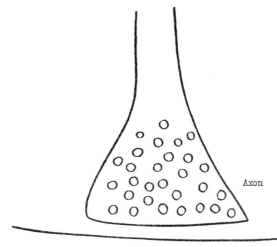

Figure 2-4. Synaptic junction showing vesicles which are supposed to contain ACh in the presynaptic axonic ending.

excited receptors of the crayfish (Grundfest, 1959). Acting in the cerebral cortex GABA inverts the activity elicited by a stimulus. Baxter and Roberts (1960) maintained that the high concentrations of GABA in brain tissue does not suggest that it plays a role as a transmitter substance; they favored it functioning to maintain the internal environment at a stable state and considered the balance between ACh and GABA to be of physiological significance. They also reported that seizures in animals were related to a pronounced decrease in GABA levels in the brain. Jasper, Khan and Elliott (1965) reported that the rate of release of GABA from the cat cortex was three times as great during sleep as during arousal periods; the rate of release of glutamic acid (the precursor of GABA) was greater in aroused than in sleeping animals. Sytivsky and Thinh (1964) found that picrotoxin-induced seizures brought a significant decrease in GABA and glutamic acid amounts in both white and grey matter of parietal cortex, and a significant decrement in GABA in occipital cortex.

These results do not show that GABA is an inhibitory transmitter; it may be an excitability modulator (Ochs, 1965).

NERVOUS SYSTEM

Description

The nervous system appears to be the most important unit underlying behavior. This system acts as a unit but for descriptive purposes it can be considered in three parts: the central, peripheral and the autonomic nervous systems. The central nervous system consists of the brain and spinal cord. Feeding into (and out of) the central system are cranial nerves and spinal nerves (peripheral system). The cranial nerves service the head region, providing information concerning these areas. The spinal nerves provide information concerning the state of the tissues over the periphery of the rest of the body and of internal organs. The autonomic nervous system consists of nervous tissue (includes a number of cranial and spinal nerves, and other tissue running parallel to the spinal cord) which is concerned with the automatic maintenance of internal states but also regulates the emotional behavior of the animal.

Information about the external world (or internal bodily states) is obtained by stimulation of receptors. The receptors are sensitive to slight changes in external and internal conditions. When the intensity of stimulation is of a certain magnitude (called threshold value) neural impulses pass to the spinal cord or brain stem and then to the upper centres. It is by means of these impulses that the organism receives information about the world, organizes his thought concerning the world and takes appropriate actions.

In a very general (and crude) sense, we can consider behavior to be regulated in a fashion as is suggested by Figure 2-5. Receptors, either on the outside or inside of the body, are activated by stimulation. Neural impulses pass over afferent fibers of the peripheral nervous system to the central nervous system. Here information provided by these impulses is integrated within the system. Finally, impulses pass over the efferent fibers of the peri-

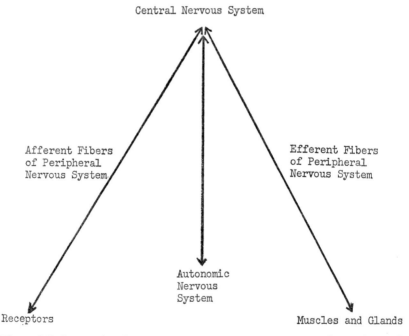

Figure 2-5. Interaction between nervous system, receptors and muscles and glands. Notice that each component influences all others, either directly or indirectly.

pheral nervous system to muscles or glands, so that action can ensue. However, this is an oversimplification of what occurs. There
is interaction between all parts of the nervous system, such that
what occurs in one portion is influenced by what is transpiring in
other parts, as is indicated by the double arrows relating the
central system to the other portions.

It is generally accepted today that the physical energies of the
external world are transformed at the receptor site into electrochemical nerve impulses which feed into an active nervous system.
Let us call this event a first order transformation. Much is known
about this process. In some manner, these electrochemical events
interact with other complex electrochemical phenomena in the
brain to bring about experiences, a second order transformation.
In this second order transformation the implanting of memory
traces and their latter reactivation are important problems, and
little factual information is available to explain this process.

The nervous system consists of a series of connections between
cells. The connections required for normal coordination develop
in prenatal life according to a biochemically determined plan
that precisely connects the nerve endings in the body to their
corresponding portions in the spinal cord and brain (Sperry,
1959). Although the connections of upper brain portions may be
capable of some modification via learning, the lower centers in the
brain stem and spinal cord are relatively fixed. Because their
function is dictated by their particular connections, they cannot
be modified significantly by learning.

Brain

The manner in which the second order transformation is accomplished so as to provide "experiences" has fascinated but
puzzled scientists for centuries. Most scientists agree that the brain
is the seat of the "mind" and that the second order transformation
would be impossible without it. However, the exact events underlying this transformation are obscure at the present time.

For our purpose the brain can be considered to consist of
three major portions: brain stem, cerebellum and cerebral hemispheres, as shown in Figure 2-6, a human brain. For comparative
purposes a rat brain is drawn in Figure 2-7. The outer portion

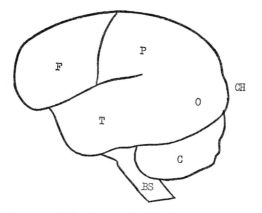

Figure 2-6. A diagram of the human brain. CH, cerebral hemisphere; BS, brain stem; C, cerebellum; F, frontal lobe; P, parietal lobe; O, occipital lobe; T, temporal lobe.

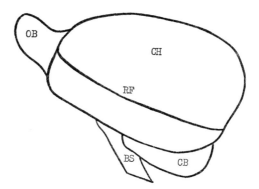

Figure 2-7. Diagram of a rat brain. OB, olfactory bulb; CH, cerebral hemisphere; CB, cerebellum; BS, brain stem; RF, rhinal fissure separating the phylogenetically newer portions of cortex (dorsal) from the older ones (ventral).

or covering of the cerebral hemispheres, the cortex, is of great importance and will be discussed below. The cerebellum is known to be important in the control and timing of motor behavior. The brain stem has received increasing concern in recent years in its connection with the conscious state or alertness of the organism, as will be indicated below.

During all activities the entire brain shows electrical excitation. No portions of the brain show a lack of excitation. However, the pattern of excitation will vary with different types of activity. Within this total excitation, specialized tissue contributes something special to the overall activity. The remaining excitatory process over the entire brain probably contributes a supportive function.

This statement is one that stresses the Gestalt or holistic viewpoint toward behavior and has been expressed by Goldstein (1948) and others. The excitation of the specialized nerve tissue is called the figure, the excitation of the supportive tissue over the rest of the brain, the background.

The exact patterns of excitation which correspond to different activities has not been determined as yet. However, research is providing more and more information concerning this problem. The electroencephalographic technique and recording of single nerve units has been especially valuable. For example, it has been found that in the normal relaxed state (with eyes closed), a person shows predominantly alpha rhythms (between 8 and 13 cycles per second) from the parietal, temporal and occipital lobes. However, upon opening his eyes the brain waves decrease in size and appear to increase in frequency in the occipital lobes. This is called the alpha block. It appears that during the relaxed state the visual cortical areas in the occipital lobes are reacting as is the rest of the brain. However, with visual stimulation occurring when the eyes are opened, the occipital cortical visual areas must now perform their function of maintaining visual events, thus changing the pattern of excitation. Likewise, blocking has occurred in the temporal lobes when the organism is stimulated with sound. During sleep, characteristic patterns of electrical excitation are found. Chemical agents modify electrical activity in a certain manner. Many other examples could be presented (Delayfresnaye, 1956; Ramey and O'Doherty, 1960; Schwab, 1951); however, behavior is varied and complex, thus making the search for electrical correlates of behavior an exceedingly difficult one. The electrical patterns for the more important activities still remain to be uncovered.

Livingston (1958) summarized the electrical activity involved in simple or complex situations in stating that when a behaving animal encounters a new situation, the recording one obtains from implanted electrodes suggests that at first a very large territory of the brain is taken up in new forms of activity, but as the experience is renewed again and again there comes about some kind of economy. He thought that the recognizable identifying signals can be reduced to a very small number of impulses, representing a tiny abstraction of reality.

Brain Interacting Units

Hughlings Jackson (cited by Head, 1926) was impressed by the hierarchy of the brain. He maintained that the more recently evolved portion, the cortex, was at the top of the hierarchy; the lowest level in the brain was the medulla in the lower part of the brain stem; in between these two levels we have other levels, the most important of which includes the thalamus and hypothalamus, at the upper end of the brain stem. He believed that each higher level imposes some control over the lower levels; this allows an increasing variety and complexity of behavior to develop. However, the higher levels of the hierarchy are less resistant to attack and are the first ones to suffer dissolution when damaged. For example, the cells of the cerebral cortex require a richer blood supply than do cells at lower levels of the hierarchy so as to maintain an adequate supply of oxygen. If the cortical cells do not receive oxygen for several minutes (anoxia), some cells will die. Cells in lower levels can exist for a longer period before they die of anoxia. Likewise, cortical cells in the newborn infant can exist in an anoxic state for a longer period than can adult cells, because the overall activity of the former is less, with less need for oxygen.

That one of the highest levels of integration is provided by operation of the cerebral cortex can be indicated by a simple example. An organizezd pattern of rage can occur in decorticate animals; however, these animals show important differences from animals who have intact cerebral cortices. The latter animals are able to maintain their rage for long periods of time, direct their anger toward objects or individuals in the environment, and have a higher threshold for rage. On the other hand, the rage pattern of decorticate animals is of short term nature, undirected and is easily provoked (Morgan and Stellar, 1950).

Integrated behavior involves the operation of the total nervous system. However, there are four important nerve structures which contribute greatly to behavior: cerebral cortex, brain stem reticular formation, limbic system, and the afferent sensory system.

Cerebral Cortex

The cortex consists of a layer of cells (six in most portions) and contributes something special in each behavioral event. The cortical areas for sensory and motor function can be localized with relatively good accuracy (Fig. 2-8). For example, in man the area important for vision is in the occipital lobes; for hearing, in the temporal lobes; for the skin senses and internal sensitivity (pressure, warm-cold), in the anterior portion of the parietal lobes. Localization of pain is not certain. Some evidence indicates that pain centers are subcortically located (in the thalamus). Other data suggest that the anterior portion of the frontal lobes is important for pain. Barber (1959) indicated that research results show that fibers of the "pain system" terminate in the brain stem, thalamus, and in widespread portions of the cerebral cortex. Cortical contributors to taste and smell are found in the lower portion of the frontal lobes and the basal portion of the temporal lobes. The main specialized tissue responsible for motor activity is located in the posterior portions of the frontal lobes but fibers contributing to motor behavior come from many portions of the cortex. Likewise, the basal ganglia (just below the cortex) are important in preventing spontaneous muscular tremors at rest, while the cerebellum integrates the muscular pattern temporally. Lesions of the basal ganglia result in tremors while resting whereas cerebellar lesions cause tremors during voluntary movements.

The cortex of higher animals such as man are highly developed such that extensive invagination or wrinkling occurs. In lower animals such as the rat the cortex is entirely smooth. Figure 2-9 indicates sensory-motor portions of the rat brain.

The more complex functions are not as accurately localized. Some effort has been made to localize these functions; however, much controversy prevails today concerning these functions. It appears safe to say that the anterior portions of the frontal lobes have some effect on sequential behavior. For example, animals

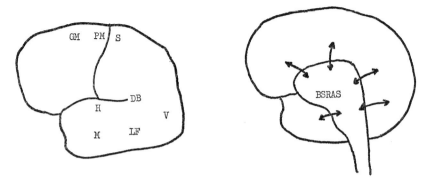

Outside View of Brain   Medial View of Brain

Figure 2-8. Diagram showing localization attempts and the interaction of the brain stem reticular activation system with other portions of the brain. GM, gross motor reactions; PM, precise motor reactions; S, somesthesis; DB, discriminative behavior; V, vision; H, hearing; M, memory; LF language formulation; BSRAS, brain stem reticular activation system.

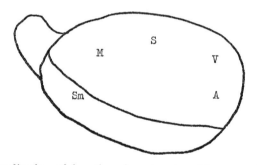

Figure 2-9. Localization of functions in rat cortex. M, motor; S, somesthesis; A, auditory; V, visual; Sm, smell.

with lesions in these areas have difficulty with sequential tasks (Pribram, 1960). Humans who undergo prefrontal lobotomy (a surgical treatment in which fibers between the frontal lobes and subcortical areas are severed) show poor ability to order and organize their activities; their behavior may deteriorate drastically in this respect.

Other tissue in the parietal, occipital and temporal lobes appears to subserve discriminative functions. Animals with lesions in these areas show great difficulty in learning maze patterns (Pribram, 1960). Penfield (1956, 1958, 1960) has found that one can reactivate vivid memory patterns of previous experiences by stimulating portions of the temporal lobes and suggests that memory may be localized there or in nearby subcortical tissue. Nielson (1946) has reported that these lobes are important for language formulation. The example above on rage also shows that the cortex contributes something special to that process. It is probable that the cortex assists in general integration of behavior along with subcortical tissues as well as providing specific functions.

Before leaving the cortex it should be pointed out that the neurons of the cortex are imbedded in a mass of supporting cells called glia. These glia cells are much more abundant than neurons (Tower, 1960) and are intimately entwined with the latter. The exact function of glia is not known but it has been assumed that a nutritive one was involved. The glia are also considered to act to prevent diffusion of some chemicals from the blood into the brain (blood-brain barrier). Other individuals (notably Galambos, Hyden, Pribram and Landauer) have assigned the neuroglia a primary role in learning. This possibility will be discussed in later chapters.

Brain Stem Reticular Formation

The brain stem consists of the medulla (next to spinal cord), pons, mesencephalon and diencephalon; the latter is further divided into the thalamus and hypothalamus. The medulla is involved in vital processes such as respiration. Damage in this portion of the stem may bring about death. This portion is also the site for the gathering of fibers going upward and downward (conduction). The pons is likewise important in upward and downward conduction. The mesencephalson is important for visual and auditory reflex behavior. The hypothalamus appears to be the site for centers which control the chemical balance of the body, having an effect on temperature regulation, emotional reactions, activity levels, motivated behavior, etc. The thalamus acts as a relay site, receiving fibers from lower centers and from the periphery, projecting them upward to the cortex and projecting fibers from cortex downward. The thalamus is in intimate relations with all parts of the cortex via these projections.

In recent years the brain stem has been receiving much attention (Magoun, 1956, 1963; and others). Scattered throughout the brain stem are clumps of cells which have been given the name, reticular formation. These cells are anatomically different but appear to be physiologically similar (Olszewski, 1956). If an animal or human is resting or sleeping and the reticular formation is stimulated electrically, the animal shows an "activation pattern." This is indicated in the EEG by an increase in the frequency of the brain rhythms, beta activity (greater than 13 cps) being dominant. On the other hand if destructive lesions are made in the upper mesencephalon or diencephalon (upper portions of the brain stem), the alert or resting animal will show a deactivating pattern, i.e., the animal will show brain waves which are characteristic of sleep or coma, the delta waves (less than 4 cps). Much research has indicated that the brain stem sends fibers to many cortical regions, some of these fibers relaying in the thalamus before projecting to the cortex while others go directly to the cortex (ascending reticular activation system). Likewise, the reticular system receives fibers back from the cortex. These up and down fibers are called nonspecific or diffuse tracts. Other fibers, the descending system, project to motor neurons in the spinal cord and to sensory receptors at the periphery of the body or at other portions of the sensory systems. The descending system can regulate the sensitivity of receptors (Hernandez-Peon, 1961; Livingston, 1958, 1959; Magoun, 1963). For example, if clicks are presented to a cat's ear, the receptors in the ear are stimulated and nerve impulses are detected in the auditory system. If a mouse is then introduced while the clicks are continued, activation occurs in the brain stem reticular system and in the visual system but the electrical activity in the auditory system is abolished or reduced. Thus the reticular system may be an important component in attention (Hernandez-Peon, 1961; Magoun, 1963) and can filter or gate the input. It appears that the diffuse reticular system contributes a facilitatory or tonic effect on behavior of long lasting nature. Variations in activity of this system have been related to degrees of consciousness, with low activity corresponding to the "unconscious" states whereas greater activity is related to the active, conscious states. Furthermore, it has been indicated that there is an optimum activity level which is consistent with best performance (Fuster, 1958; Hebb, 1955; Lindsley, 1960). When there is too little activity of these cells, the animal will sleep; when too great activity, the animal becomes emotional and rigid in his behavior.

Some individuals have attempted to localize a center for integration of the diffuse system in the thalamus, in the upper reticular formation. Penfield (1956, 1958, 1960) suggested that sensory information is integrated by this *centrencephalic system*. A selected portion of the sensory information is projected to the temporal cortex so that comparisons of present experiences can be made with past experiences whose traces are supposed to be housed in the temporal cortex or nearby ganglionic portions. Thus overall integration involved up-and-down projections between the centrencephalic system in the thalamus and other portions of the brain and the periphery of the body. Penfield chose the thalamic area as the focal tissue for the centrencephalic system because he desired brain tissue which had equal functional relationship with both hemispheres and whose stimulation or destruction brought widespread effects.

Jasper's views (1956, 1958, 1960) are somewhat similar to those of Penfield. He maintained that functional integration probably takes places by means of the corpus callosum (fibers which go from one hemisphere to the other) or by cortico-subcortical projection systems below the thalamus, with the latter most likely. He indicated that the thalamic reticular system was unique in the regulation of electrical activity of the brain. By stimulating a small portion of this system, widespread areas of the cortex were caused to beat in rhythmic synchrony. In no other portions of the reticular system was it possible to achieve such results. He suggested (1958) that the function of this reticular system was to prevent a general arousal reaction to all stimuli and to provide selective responsiveness to significant stimuli; thus he emphasized inhibitory functions as more important than excitatory ones either during sleep or wakefulness.

Jasper (1960) claimed that the thalamic reticular system was the most important regulator of spontaneous electrical activity of the entire cortex and was capable of some local effects which might give it a more highly integrated function than the lower reticular system. The upper system appeared to mediate a more rapid but shorter-lasting cortical excitation than the lower system. He referred to this excitation as the phasic type of activation, as opposed to the tonic activation from the lower portions of the system.

Lindsley (1958) maintained that general arousal was mediated by the lower portion of the reticular formation. On the other hand, general alerting and specific alerting reactions of a waking animal were subserved by the upper portions of the reticular formation in conjunction with certain thalamic nuclei and the diffuse thalamocortical projection system. He indicated that some portions of the reticular system can be aroused by any sensory stimulation but that some are excited by one type of sense modality but not by others. Stimulation of certain cortical sites resulted in excitation in the reticular formation; maximal response in the reticular formation had different latencies for different cortical areas. He concluded that such results not only opens the possibility for augmentation and inhibition of reticular activity, but provides a basis for understanding the mechanisms of attention, conditioning and perception.

Numerous others (e.g., Gastaut, 1958; Green, 1960; Magoun, 1963) have expressed somewhat similar viewpoints. Thus, as an oversimplification, it appears that the lower portions of the reticular system contribute a general effect on consciousness and behavior of lasting nature whereas the upper portion has a shorter, more specific effect.

Limbic System

The limbic system is an ill-defined portion of the brain which usually includes cortical and subcortical tissue that is located around the core of the brain, i.e., around the upper brain stem. The inner or basal portion of the ventral cortex is an important component in this system. The hippocampal area which has been implicated in memory events (Bremer, 1960; Gerard, 1960) is located toward the posterior portion of the basal ventral cortex in rats but extends forward in humans and is considered to be involved in a high level of integration (Green, 1960). The amygdala (a subcortical nucleus) is located toward the medial portion of the ventral cortical area. This nucleus is considered of importance in integration and is also assumed to be involved in memory aspects (Gerard, 1960).

A recent summary of the functions of the amygdala (Goddard, 1964) indicated that it receives input from all sensory modalities, various portions of the cortex, reticular formation, hippocampus, cerebellum and thalamus. The amygdala, in turn, projects to most subcortical midline structures and to widespread portions of the cortex. Goddard reported that evidence shows that the amygdala is important in the regulation of drives, especially fear, but is not essential for their elaboration, and is involved in the suppression of motivated approach behavior and in the association of fear and avoidance behavior with previously neutral stimuli.

The limbic system has widespread connections with the rest of the brain, especially the hypothalamus, thalamus, reticular system of the mesencephalon and frontal lobes. Via these widespread connections the limbic system is assumed to contribute to emotional and motivational behavior.

The hypothalamus is considered to be important in motivated and numerous other behaviors (Olds, 1956; Stellar, 1960). For example, stimulation or lesions in specific portions can induce eating, produce rage, induce sexual behavior, affect body temperature, etc. However, to complicate the picture, Grossman (1964) has shown that cholinergic chemicals (ACh and similar substances) injected in the lateral hypothalamus can elicit drinking behavior whereas adrenergic substances (adrenalin type chemicals) in the same site will arouse feeding behavior.

Adey (1958) suggested that the hippocampus and other anterior limbic structures were intimately connected with the thalamic reticular system, and the amygdala and entorhinal cortex (posterior ventral cortex) project to the midbrain reticular formation. Thus the limbic system exerts an influence on, and in turn is influenced by, the activity of the upper and lower reticular system.

The limbic system has also been shown to have an effect on the pituitary gland (Mason, 1958) ; thus the endocrine system with its widespread effect on behavior appears to be connected to the reticular system and limbic system, with the hippocampus and amygdala as the important portions of the latter which affect endocrine activity.

Sensory Systems

It has been known for many years that a certain excitability level is required to maintain an animal in a waking state. Numerous clinical reports have indicated that patients will fall asleep if deprived of sensory input and can be aroused only by stimulation of some sense organs. Experimental evidence indicates that the afferent impulses necessary for keeping the cerebral cortex in a state of vigilance reach it from the reticular formation (Chang, 1959). When the receptors for the various senses are stimulated, internally or externally, nerve impulses pass throughout the nervous pathways to the brain. These are called specific tracts. As these afferent pathways proceed to the cortex via the thalamus, they are assumed to give off collateral fibers to the reticular formation in the brain stem. It appears that the sensory input collateral tracts aid the reticular cells in performing their facilitatory or "tone" effect on the higher centers, specifically the cerebral cortex.

These functions have been best illustrated by experimental studies wherein sensory input was reduced. For example, studies at McGill University were conducted to investigate the behavior of individuals confirmed to small spaces wherein sensory stimulation (visually, aurally and kinesthetically) were minimized. The subjects were paid $20.00 a day to do nothing but to lie on a comfortable bed in a small cubicle with the eyes, ears and hands shielded to reduce the sensory input from the environment. The subjects wore goggles which permitted only diffuse light; cardboard cuffs extending below the fingertips maintained tactile stimulation at a monotonous level. Auditory stimulation was minimized by the continuous hum of a fan, an air conditioner and an amplifier. The individual left the cubicle only to eat or for elimination needs. Few subjects endured the task for more than two or three days; six days was the maximum. The investigators maintained that even though the subjects were in need of money, they left this task for other jobs which paid much less but demanded much more in mental and physical activity, apparently indicating an overwhelming need to be exposed to patterned and varying stimulus input of almost any kind (Bexton *et al.,* 1954; Heron, 1957; Heron *et al.,* 1956.)

The investigations indicated that decrements in performance and various abnormal phenomena may occur. Concentration, ability to carry on organized thinking and various intellectual tasks were adversely affected. Visual, aural and tactual hallucinations were reported. The hallucinations of some subjects involved sequences of geometric forms. In some cases the frequency of the spontaneous electrical activity of the brain decreased.

Numerous other studies involving a reduction in the quantity of sensory input or lack of variability in the input have shown, in general, similar results although the tendency for hallucinations and performance decrements is not always so prominent (Solomon *et al.,* 1961; Zuckerman and Cohen, 1964) .

The conclusion from these experiments is that a varied sensory input is required for integrated behavior to occur. Hebb (1955) maintained that sensory input serves two functions. The first is to maintain tonicity of the reticular system. If input is decreased or not varied, the activity of the reticular system will decrease. This is essentially what happens when we go to sleep. We seek an environment where sensory input will be decreased and involve little variation. The second function of the sensory input is to provide information or cues about external objects and does not involve the reticular formation. Rather, this function is subserved by tissue at higher levels, e.g., visual cues — by means of the occipital lobes, auditory cues — through operation of certain tissue in the temporal lobes, etc.

The cortex, reticular formation, limbic system and specific afferent system cooperate in the overall integration of behavior. A few years ago it was believed that in the integration of behavior, the neural impulses would pass to the thalamus, thence to the cortex, e.g., to the occipital lobes for visual information. To bring about integrated behavior following stimulation of the occipital lobes, it was believed that short intracortical fibers brought about activation of nearby association areas in the temporal, occipital and parietal lobes or to association areas in the frontal lobes. These association areas were supposed to be involved in the complex aspects of behavior such as thinking, learning and reasoning. Then excitation would spread to the motor areas in the posterior portion of the frontal lobes and motor behavior would result.

Today the importance of short intracortical fibers is less stressed (Penfield, 1960). The evidence suggests that the sensory areas of the cortex are stimulated as indicated above. However, projections downward to the thalamus and upward again to other cortical areas are emphasized. The up and down projections between the thalamus and cortex provide for a complex integrating system with the thalamus as a center (Penfield, 1956, 1958, 1960). For example, in visual tasks the occipital cortex is stimulated via the afferent sensory system. Fibers from the occipital lobe project to the thalamus. Other fibers project upward to the anterior and posterior association areas, allowing something special to be added to the complex process. Fibers project downward to the thalamus, thence upward to the motor areas in the frontal lobes and finally downward to the spinal cord and to the muscles, bringing about an overall integrated pattern of behavior.

CHAPTER 3

LEARNING

LEARNING PHENOMENA

LEARNING EVENTS have been of much concern to molecular psychobiologists. Learning is a complex phenomenon which includes a number of events, *viz.*, acquisition, short- and long-term memory, reactivation, normal forgetting, unusual forgetting, and integration. Of these the memory events are the most basic in that the others utilize memory. Likewise, these are the simplest to deal with; the other phenomena present real stumbling blocks to theoretical treatment except at the psychological level. Thus many theorists avoid these events.

Acquisition

When an organism first encounters a learning task, his behavior is variable and erratic. For example, the hungry rat placed in a complex T maze will enter many blind alleys and move slowly through the maze. After a number of trials, however, his behavior is smoother, i.e., he runs quickly to the appropriate arm containing the food. Humans in a similar situation show the same change in behavior as a result of specific experiences. Thus, learning can be diagrammed as follows:

$$X \xrightarrow{\text{experience}} X'$$

The organism is naive (X) but as a result of experience he is changed (X') such that if he is again exposed to the stimulating conditions he will indicate this change in his behavior.

Memory

After the organism is removed from the stimulating conditions, he carries some representation of his experiences with him, a "memory trace." A dual process of memory has been advocated by a number of individuals. It has been suggested that transient or short-term memory depends on reverberating circuits in the brain whereas changes in synaptic regions as a result of reverberation provides for permanent or long-term memory. The dual process, however, may be an oversimplification.

Reactivation

After a memory has been established there is some mechanism which allows the organism to activate the "trace" so that he can remember or recall the experience for which the "trace" has been established.

Normal Forgetting

Over a period of time one finds that his memory for earlier learning events becomes less clear. However, the time aspect is important mainly because of the activities in which the organism indulges during this period. This reduction in memory clearness is called retroactive interference or inhibition.

Unusual Forgetting

Forgetting of specific portions of one's experiences may occur in hypnosis, repression and amnesia. For example, a man may unconsciously hate his wife but be unable to express this feeling directly. However, it might be shown by a sudden complete lack of recognition of his wife and any events related to her. This selective forgetting is extremely difficult for theorists to handle.

Integration

For new learning to occur, the organism must reactivate memory traces of previous events and order them in some meaningful manner relative to the environment at the moment.

VARIOUS APPROACHES TO LEARNING

General

The topic of learning is a central problem for behavioral scientists. Although the topic has traditionally been a problem mainly for psychologists, it appears that the solution (i.e., an understanding of learning) will not be a psychological one but will require recourse to neurological and neurochemical concepts. The major learning approaches have been the treatments within a psychological frame of reference exemplified by Thorndike, Hull, Guthrie, Skinner, the Gestaltists, Tolman and others. However, in recent years a number of other approaches have appeared on the scene, *viz.*, mathematical, analogical, neurological and neurochemical.

The mathematical (or symbolic) approach to learning which has generated much research in recent years has been of a probability or stochastic nature (e.g., Bush and Mosteller, 1955; Estes, 1950; Overall, 1960; Restle, 1955). These mathematical models have served as convenient guides and have provided valuable insights concerning learning phenomena.

In recent years science has been permeated by a rash of models in which different types of analogies provide insight into the functioning of the organism. The main concern of some of these models has not been with learning; however, most of these analogies can include learning phenomena. These analogues include communication models (Miller, 1953), servomechanisms (Weiner, 1948), computer models (Rosenblatt, 1958), mechanical models (Broadbent, 1957), and others. These models, like the mathematical approach, have provided interesting and ingenious ideas concerning behavior.

Both the mathematical and analogical approaches are of extra-organismic nature, i.e., they utilize external aspects to apply to the organism. On the other hand, the neurological and neurochemical approaches are intraorganismic in that they deal directly with the internal aspects of the organism.

The neurological approaches to learning have been numerous. The most influential ones have been those by Lashley (1929) and by Hebb (1949). The cell assemblies and phase sequences of the latter have permeated much of psychological thinking. Pribram (1960) has presented an interesting theoretical approach in an excellent review. Other excellent reviews of research on learning phenomena include articles by Morrell (1961), John (1961) and Thomas (1962). Neurological aspects will be considered below.

The neurochemical approach to learning is a very recent one and appears to offer great promise for the future. In this area some very exciting research results have been obtained. This approach is that to which most of the later chapters will be devoted and a preliminary treatment will be introduced below.

It is hoped that future investigations on learning will relate psychological occurrences to those at the neurological and bio-chemical levels. Events are transpiring simultaneously at each of these levels; thus one has a type of nominal isomorphism in which each event in the psychological level has a corresponding event in the neurological and neurochemical levels, i.e., one can map the events in the psychological domain into those of the neurological and neurochemical domains. Such mapping will not only allow for interesting relationships between the levels but should provide for insights concerning the relationships within each level. For example, if the relationships between events on the psychological level are well known and the isomorphs of a number of these are available on the other two levels, the remaining intra- and inter-level isomorphs then would be easier to uncover.

Neurological

There have been a number of attempts to specify the neuro-logical structure which is modified during learning and which provides the basis for memory. It appears that the site which is chosen usually by theorists is the synapse. Recently, however, especially with the neurochemical approach, interest has shifted to the soma of the nerve cell. Yet both sites are probably of im-portance during learning.

Hebb (1961) has indicated that it is not only important to understand the role of the synapse in learning but the concurrent activity of the total central nervous system must be considered. The first problem is more "molecular" and physiological, being concerned with the relations between two individual neurons; the other is "molar" and psychological, involving operations of the total system. One could consider that these are behavior regulating events, the first of intercell nature whereas the second would be of intersystems nature. However, for a complete picture another regulatory system should be considered, the intracellular one. This would be a "submolecular" and chemical treatment.

Hebb (1949) developed a theoretical model of brain function

which has influenced to some degree all scientists interested in this topic. He maintained that the stimulation involved in an experience would excite certain cells in the brain, which would then represent that experience. If the experience is not repeated, the excitation would stop and nothing would be available as a symbol of the experience. However, if the stimulation were repeated frequently, a "cell assembly" would slowly develop. The cell assembly consisted of a number of cells in the cortex and diencephalon (and possibly in other subcortical cells as well) which could act briefly as a closed, reverberating circuit. Hebb believed that this brief reverberation could be the basis for short term memory. If the reverberation continued for a longer period of time (which he did not specify definitively), the electrical excitation caused neural growth to occur, which provided the basis for long term memory. This growth was supposed to occur at the presynaptic terminal and would increase the area of functional contact between this portion and the cell upon which it impinged. Hebb called a series of cell assemblies a "phase sequence." He used cell assemblies and phase sequences as the basis for all simple and complex functions. The emphasis was on excitatory circuits but Milner (1957) added inhibitory elements to strengthen the theory.

Thus the original Hebbian approach involved a dual process for learning: reverberation for short term memory and synaptic growth for permanent memory. Hebb (1961) added a third process for another short term memory, memory for highly familiar materials. For example, if one is presented with a series of digits he can remember them for a short period of time and then they can no longer be reproduced. This suggests that reverberation ceases before modification has occurred. However, if one is presented with a series of multiple digits in which one set of digits is repeated on every third presentation in the series, the person is able to maintain these for a longer period of time. If reverberation is responsible for memory for the numbers, the reverberation should be disrupted by the reverberation of the two series of numbers following the critical one. Thus Hebb suggested that no reverberation occurs in these memory events. Instead he postulated a process which involves synapses which have extensive connections already developed gaining temporary dominance over others.

A somewhat similar approach was that by Konorski (1948). He advocated anatomical changes at the synapse during learning. Somewhat similar ideas were expressed by a number of individuals at the Hixon Symposium (Jeffress, 1951) and at the Laurentian Symposium (Delayfresnaye, 1956). Likewise, Gerard (1953) mentioned a number of events which he believed might provide the synaptic changes which facilitate learning and maintain memory, *viz.*, swelling of terminal elements while conducting impulses, alterations in electrical potential, actual neural growth at synapse and changes in nerve proteins. Eccles (1958) presented a somewhat similar view.

The dual process for memory events has received some support from research and theoretical efforts. Gerard (1953) was one of the earliest individuals to suggest a dual process of memory. Morrell (1961, p. 478) cited data by Chow which are consistent with this possibility. Chow reported that electrical changes in neural tissue were detected only during the early stages of conditioning. Morrell uses these results, as well as others indicating that memory survives convulsions, electroshock, trauma, concussion and deep anesthesia, to implicate RNA as a possible durable memory molecule. Likewise, John (1961, p. 465) stated that reverberatory circuits could be the basis for short-term memory but that long-term memory would seem to necessitate s structural modification, a "consolidation" of the memory trace.

That some type of "consolidation" occurs following short term memory events appears plausible because of experimental data. For example, experiments have shown that individuals who learn something and then go to sleep tend to retain more than do individuals who do not sleep after learning (Crafts, Schneirla, Robinson and Gilbert, 1950). In this case the period of sleep or relative inactivity presumably would reduce interference with "consolidation." Gerard (1953) reported a similar experiment with hamsters. Hamsters learned a maze habit, had the body temperature cooled so that hibernation ensued and after recovering showed that they remembered the maze pattern.

The results of disruption of the "consolidation process" by shocking animals after learning trials with electroconvulsive shock (ECS), is consistent with the notion of reverberatory circuits or some similar event. Duncan (1949) trained rats to avoid shock to the feet in a shuttle box by running from one end of the box to the other. A light (conditioned stimulus) was turned on ten seconds prior to the shock. Nine groups of animals were used: one received no ECS after learning but each of the other groups reached ECS, the trial-ECS interval varying from twenty seconds to fourteen hours. The animals were later placed in the shuttle-box and their behavior noted. The results clearly indicated an effect of ECS on performance; the magnitude of the effect decreased as the interval increased, i.e., the greater the time interval between learning trial and ECS, the greater the number of avoidance responses.

Similar results have been obtained by other investigators. Thompson (1958) used a visual discrimination task and found that ECS produces a greater decrement in young than adult rats. Thompson and Pennington (1957) reported that a single ECS after massed trials produced a greater memory decrement than after spaced trials, presumably because spaced trials allowed "consolidation" to proceed for a longer uninterrupted period than did the massed trials.

The interpretation of these results as indicating a "consolidation process" have been questioned by several individuals (Coons and Miller, 1960; Adams and Lewis, 1962; Lewis and Maher, 1965) who maintained that ECS is punishing and that animals perform poorly when ECS is given after training because cues associated with the ECS situation arouse fear or interfering responses such as trembling and crouching or conditioned inhibition develops. However, McGaugh has indicated by a number of studies that the consolidation hypothesis is still a suitable interpretation of the ECS results. In one study (Madsen and McGaugh, 1961) all rats received an intense shock when they stepped off a small platform onto a grid floor. Half of the animals then received ECS. When tested twenty-four hours later these animals acted as if they had not been punished at all. In another study (Hudspeth, McGaugh and Thomson, 1964), repeated ECS treatments were involved. Four groups of rats were used: no shock, foot shock, ECS and foot shocks followed by ECS after each trial. The results indicated that repetitive ECS treatments did have a punishing effect but considerably less than was that of foot shock punishment. Other experiments (McGaugh and Madsen, 1964) showed also that ECS treatments produced retrograde amnesia but when repeated were somewhat punishing. However, the overall results were consistent with the consolidation hypothesis. Other experimental results are consistent with a consolidation interpretation, e.g., Gerbrandt and Thomson (1964), Leonard and Zavala (1964), and Tenen (1965).

One problem with the ECS studies is that researchers have theorized about neurophysiological events in the brain during learning but have not attempted to determine experimentally the nervous system reactions which accompany the behavioral events. An adequate evaluation of the consolidation hypothesis would require information from three levels, behavioral, neurological and biochemical. One interesting theoretical paper (Hudspeth and Gerbrandt, 1965) has attempted to incorporate ECS data and certain electrophysiological relations during the development of conditioned responses.

In this context, it is interesting that a few studies (discussed in Chapter 8) show that experimentally induced convulsions (by ECS and Metrazol) ultimately decrease the amount of RNA available throughout the brain but does not effect the DNA content. Within fifteen seconds there is a slight increase in RNA content; thirty seconds after induction the RNA amounts are similar to those of control animals; at seventy-five seconds there is a moderate decrease and at about five minutes the decreases are between ten and thirty per cent throughout the brain and spinal cord. These decreases are probably of significance; however, convulsions obviously affect other cellular systems such that the effect of RNA decrease would be difficult to disentangle from the effect of other disruptions. For example, approximately 44 per cent losses occur in ACh brain content as a result of seizures (Takahashi and Aprison, 1964).

McGaugh (1964) has also indicated that memory storage can be facilitated by drugs. McGaugh, Jennings and Thomson (1962) had shown that maze-bright rats are superior in maze learning to maze-dull rats only in massed trials. If the trials were spaced five minutes or more apart, the two groups of animals were not significantly different. Thus they reasoned that the two groups differed in the rate of neural consolidation. The difference in the two strains was also eradicated by injections of the neural stimulant 5-7-diphenyl-1-3 diazadamantan-6-01 (McGaugh, Westbrook and Burt, 1961), the drug having the same effect as separating the trials. Other neural stimulants such as strychnine sulfate and picrotoxin have facilitated learning also. Similar results were reported by Pearlman (1963). Hudspeth (1964) found that strychnine had a facilitative effect on learning of a brightness discrimination problem as well.

Some drugs appear to disrupt the consolidation process. Pearlman, Sharpless and Jarvik (1961) found that anaesthetization with ether or pentobarbital had the same effect as did ECS. If the drug was given immediately after the learning trial, a profound effect on retention occurred. If the drug treatment was given fifteen minutes after the trial, however, there was no effect.

Other procedures have supported the idea that some type of vulnerable, transient physiological process underlies short term memory. These include functional decortication by spreading cortical depression produced by potassium chloride (Bures and Buresova, 1963; Ray and Emley, 1964, 1965), low-frequency stimulation of the caudate nucleus (Wyers, 1963), electrical stimulation of reticular formation (Glickman, 1958), and cholinergic stimulation in thalamic reticular nuclei (Grossman, 1964; Miller, 1965).

Pribram (1963) suggested that glia might function during the consolidation period as storage devices. Their electrical responsivity is some thousandfold longer in duration than that of neural units. Such graded electrical activity could influence the transmitted excitations of the adjacent neural circuits which in turn could affect the state of the glia. The joint excitation of glia and neurons would direct fiber growth with the glia forming the matrix into which nerve cell fiber growth would occur. This was a glial guided-neural growth hypothesis.

These results appear to indicate that some transient activity is responsible for memory, and if other activities intervene there is less chance for the permanent changes to occur. Likewise, observations with elderly individuals support the notion of short-term processes. In these people we know that the brain tissue is less plastic, and hardening of blood vessels and other tissues occurs. If the tissue is less plastic, then it would seem that the initial reverberatory circuits or similar short-term events would be less effective in developing neural changes. Thus the retention of the learning of new materials would be less than when the individual were younger. This is exactly what one finds with elderly persons, with difficulty in the learning of new materials and quick forgetting of newly learned material.

Other individuals have also suggested a dual process for memory. For example, Dethier and Stellar (1961) maintained that brain-damaged studies with man and animal-learning experiments involving shock suggest that memory is a two-part process: an initial, vulnerable process lasting fifteen minutes to an hour; and a later, invulnerable process providing the permanent basis for memory.

Glickman (1961) suggested essentially the same, a reverberatory circuit hypothesis for consolidation of memory traces. He cited work by Burns (1954, 1958) which is consistent with the hypothesis. Burns isolated small areas of the cortex and noted their responses to electrical stimulation. He found that single trains of pulses can initiate activity lasting for thirty minutes or more, that later electrical stimulation interferes with this activity, and that the activity becomes easier to evoke with repetitions of the stimulus.

Even though some individuals have questioned only a single short-term process and a single long-term memory (Heeb, 1961; Gerard, 1963; Pribram, 1963b), the dual process hypothesis is still an attractive one. However, the hypothesis is probably an oversimplification which can be tolerated at this stage of knowledge. The two are on a time continuum, and the chemical events prior to the stabilizing of traces may quickly run their course in some cases but require more sustained activity in other cases. Thus short term memory might be measured in seconds, minutes or days with the intermediary chemical events maintaining the trace during this period.

The use of the electrophysiological approach to locate brain tissue involved in learning events has been employed by numerous investigators. However, as Brazier (1960) and others (e.g., John, 1961; Morrell, 1961) have cogently indicated, it is improbable that electrical signs will be associated with permanent memory but electrical activity should occur when a memory is being made lop and Hendrix, 1960; Holmes and Adey, 1960) implicated the or evoked.

Studies by Adey and his colleagues (Adey, 1960; Adey, Dunlop and Hendrix, 1960; Holmes and Adey, 1960) implicated the hippocampus and nearby structures, the amygdala and the entorhinal cortex, in learning events. They implanted electrodes in the brains of cats; the cats were exposed to a T maze or an apparatus in which a food box was placed at each of the two ends. Only one of the boxes contained food. When the animals were first exposed to the apparatus and approached the goal box, a wide spectrum of sustained hippocampal and entorhinal slow wave activity at 4 to 7 cps was observed; as conditioning proceeded there was rapid stabilization of rhythmic activity in the dorsal hippocampus and entorhinal area at 6 cps. The 4 to 7 cps activity disappeared from the ventral hippocampus early in training. The 6 cps activity persisted throughout training, was not present during intertrial intrials, but a strong 4 cps burst occurred and in late training was maximal in the entorhinal area. It disappeared during extinction of the goal directed response and reappeared during retraining. By an analysis of the phase relationships they deduced that, in the untrained animal, passage of activity was from the hippocampus to entorhinal area; in the trained animal the hippocampus activity was subsequent to that of the entorhinal structures.

Adey and his colleagues suggested that the 4 to 7 cps rhythm represents a readiness to act and that the changing slow wave patterns actively subserve the integration of information. However, they suggested that the memory trace was not recorded in the hippocampus but that this structure provided the appropriate triggering for the deposition of the trace in other neural systems.

Grastyan (1959) reported slow activity in the hippocampus during learning also. He suggested that the rhythmic slow activity indicated the hippocampal participation in the formation of temporary connections; the development of slow waves early in conditioning indicated the involvement of the reticular formation in that stimulation of the latter evokes hippocampal slow waves. One of the main functions of the hippocampus was to inhibit the initial widespread discharge of the reticular formation.

During the approach to the goal in the Adey experiments there was a typical burst of electrical activity in the amygdala at 40 cps which showed little or no correlation with the hippocampal activity; it disappeared only briefly at the attainment of the food reward but continued indefinitely as the animal's hunger approached satiety.

The hippocampal and nearby tissue has long been considered important in memory, as well as for other behaviors. Confusion, diminished awareness, amnesia and automatic behavior upon direct stimulation of hippocampal structures in man have been reported. Penfield (1958) indicated that no permanent record of experience was possible after removal of the hippocampus and nearby tissue.

Pribram (1960, 1963a) suggested that these limbic areas affect memory because they are important for the execution of behavior sequences, particularly those involved in feeding, fleeing, fighting, mating and maternal behavior. A number of experiments have tended to substantiate his claim. For example, Kimble and Pribram (1963) reported that bilateral hippocampal lesions in monkeys produced no decrement of simple memory in visual discrimination tasks, but did effect impairment in the acquisition of behaviors which involve the execution of sequential responses. Kimble (1963) found that bilaterally hippocampectomized rats when compared with normal rats showed a greater incidence of repetitive running in an open field situation, poorer performance on a *successive* brightness discrimination task, and a greater number of errors in a complex maze requiring sequential behavior.

Characteristic electrical activity has been reported from other structures during conditioning; Guzman-Flores *et al.* (1965)

found a hypersynchronous rhythm of 12 to 17 cps in the visual cortex and reticular formation of cats during the early stages of visual learning. At the establishment of the conditional response, the hypersynchrony disappeared and was observed in isolated bursts during the intertrial intervals only. Five cps activity has been observed in the reticular formation, certain midline thalamic nuclei, and in the caudate nucleus shortly after the pairing of the CS and the US. The caudate nucleus apparently operates as a portion of a cortical-caudate-thalamus inhibitory system (Wyers, 1963).

Thus there is much evidence to suggest that specific electrical patterns accompany learning events with widespread excitatory and inhibitory effects in the brain; however, a real problem is to determine what there patterns mean in terms of actual sequential functions.

Neurochemical

General

The neurochemical approach to behavior may be said to have had its inception when Thudichum published a monumental treatise (Thudichum, 1884; cited by Page, 1955). Thudichum described the first systematic attempt to understand the chemical mechanisms of nervous tissue. After Thudichum's death in 1901, work on neurochemistry all but stopped. Approximately thirty-five years later, scientists again began to study the chemical mechanisms of nerve tissue.

In recent years this renewed interest in neurochemistry has been reflected by a number of results which have been pertinent to behavior. For example, Williams (1956) investigated the biochemical make-up of humans and lower animals and indicated that underlying the differences in behavior of organisms are differences in chemical activity. An exciting neurochemical approach is the attempt to identify specific chemicals such as serotonin, adrenolution, ACh, etc., as the causative agents for psychotic behavior (Rinkel and Denber, 1958; Rubin, 1959, 1962; Woolley, 1962). Investigations concerning the effects of chemicals on neural tissue and behavior has been accelerated by the ability to inject minute amounts in localized areas of the brain by micro-electrodes (Fisher, 1964; Grossman, 1964). Contributions in this area have been great and a formal discipline called "psychopharmacology" has developed in recent years (Russell, 1964).

The neurochemical approach to learning is extremely new, having developed within the past fifteen years. There have been two major treatments of learning within this approach, one concerned with synaptic chemistry whereas the other is concerned with intracellular molecular chemistry. The latter is the molecular psychobiological approach.

Synaptic Approach

The synapse has been considered by many theorists as playing an important role in memory. However, because of meager neurochemical data individuals have been unable to specify the exact mechanisms whereby stimulation leads to a representation of experience. For example, Gerard (1953) suggested that nerve impulses would alter protein molecules at the synapse in some unknown manner such that the altered protein composition would aid or hinder the passage of later nerve impulses.

A systematic investigation concerning the neurochemistry of the synapse was begun in the early fifties by the California group (Krech, Rosenzweig and others). They were concerned with the relationship of ACh-AChE activity and acquisition and retention of specific behavior indicative of learning. Their general hypothesis was that variation in this chemical system was a major determinant of adaptive behavior. Their specific thesis was that changes in ACh are related to learning and adaptive behavior. They conducted a series of experiments combining biochemical analytic techniques and psychological procedures. They hypothesized that experience and training may significantly alter the concentration of brain ACh and AChE (Bennett, Rosenzweig, Krech, Karlsson, Dye and Ohlander, 1958; Bennett, Krech, Rosenzweig, Karlsson, Dye and Ohlander, 1958; Krech, Rosenzweig, Bennett and Krueckel, 1954; Krech, Rosenzweig and Bennett, 1956, 1959; Krech, Rosenzweig, Bennett and Longueil, 1959; Rosenzweig, Krech and Bennett, 1956, 1960). These individuals maintained that transmission of nerve impulses is accomplished by the discharge of ACh from presynaptic neurons. Inactivation of ACh by AChE, as soon as the former stimulates the postsynaptic neuron, preserves discrete transmission of impulses.

The California group was interested in the relationship between ACh and behavior. However, no reliable techniques for the measurement of ACh were available because of its rapid metabolism. Therefore, they decided to use amounts of AChE as an index of ACh levels because the former was considered to be a stable component which is easily and reliably measured. This decision was a tentative one made with some misgivings. The procedures involved decapitating an animal, taking samples from desired portions of the brain (of rats), weighing the sample and homogenizing the tissue in certain chemicals. After homogenizing the tissue, a number of complex chemical reactions were involved; the end result being a statement of the AChE activity per milligram of tissue.

The initial study by the group indicated that rats with strong spatial (right or left) preferences in maze running had greater AChE activity than rats with strong visual (light or dark) preferences (Krech *et al.*, 1954). The greater AChE activity was present in somesthetic, visual and motor areas of the cortex. These results were confirmed in a later experiment in which pentobarbital sodium was administered to depress ACh metabolism. Animals given the drug consistently showed visual preferences (Rosenzweig *et al.*, 1956). Further results were in agreement with the first experiment (Krech *et al.*, 1956).

A very interesting result was obtained when Bennett, Rosenzweig, Krech, Karlsson, Dye and Ohlander (1958) studied the AChE activity of two strains of rats at various ages. It was found that descendants of the Tryon Maze-Bright strain showed greater average AChE activity than did descendants of the Tryon Maze-Dull strain for all ages investigated (twenty-nine to five-hundred-twenty-seven days). The curves for both strains over days showed a rapid rise, reaching a peak at approximately seventy-five to one-hundred days, and then gradually decreasing. The two curves are remarkably similar to the curve of mental growth reported for humans (Wechsler, 1944). However, the similarity may be coincidental.

Another experiment indicated that subcortical AChE activity was negatively related to brain weight, but there was no relationship between cortical AChE and brain weight (Krech, Rosenzweig and Bennett, 1959).

In 1960 Rosenzweig, Krech and Bennett rejected their hypothesis that AChE activity furnishes a good index of ACh activity. They maintained that each is under separate genetic control. However, their basic hypothesis that the ACh transmission system is intimately involved in learning was retained. This change was necessitated by results which showed that for some strains of rats high AChE levels was positively related to learning ability, but in other strains there was a negative relationship. Further experiments suggested that the difference between ACh and AChE levels was of major importance, with greater learning ability being related to greater amount of ACh (within limits) at the synapse.

The experimental work conducted by Krech and associates lends credibility to their hypothesis. However, Tower (1958) raised questions concerning the approach. He maintained that even though evidence favors ACh as the transmitter substance, the idea is controversial; ACh seems to be of less or no importance to certain systems, including much of the sensory functions upon which maze behavior is dependent; the approach does not differentiate between AChE and cholinesterase (ChE) but only the former participates in ACh hydrolysis; AChE in the brain is far in excess of requirements, thus making difficult the uncovering of relationships with activity; the changes in AChE are so small as to be possible errors of sampling and analysis. Rosenzweig, Krech and Bennett (1960) countered this last criticism by indicating that even though the differences they have found are small, these have appeared consistently.

Further work by the California group has handled more of these criticisms and they have reported further outstanding results. In a series of experiments they have provided varying degrees of experience for rats and noted the effect on brain chemistry (Rosenzweig, 1964). One group of young rats (ten to twelve) lived in a large home cage and played with "toys." Every day they explored an open field apparatus. After thirty days, formal training in mazes and problem solving apparatus was instituted. Another group of rats (isolation controls) lived in individual cages where they could not see or touch another animal. The isolation cages were opened a few times a week for addition of food, and about once a week for weighing. In some experiments a third group of rats was employed, with conditions which were intermediate between the greatly stimulated and isolated animals. These conditions were maintained for about eighty days, from twenty-five to 105 days of age. The animals given enriched experience developed brains which were different from those in the impoverished environment. The enriched experience animals had

1) Heavier and thicker cerebral cortices
2) Greater total AChE activity throughout the brain
3) Greater ChE activity in the cortex but not in the subcortex.

The animals in the intermediate condition had brain measures which were intermediate between the extreme groups in most cases. The increased stimulation also led to improved problem solving ability. There was some tendency for this condition to lead to an increase in the ratio of the number of glial cells to the number of neurons in both visual and somesthetic areas.

A recent paper (Bennett *et al.,* 1964) reported similar results, plus new ones. Enriched environmental training was instituted at about 105 days of age. The adult brain showed increases in cortical weight and AChE as was the case for the animals given enrichment at a young age. These results showed that the brain changes in anatomy and chemistry were not a function of accelerated early development but were an effect of experience.

In other experiments animals were blinded at twenty-five days of age. After about eighty days in an enriched environment, blinded animals had 5 per cent less weight in the visual cortex and 8 per cent less in the superior colliculi than did their seeing littermates. Total AChE activity increased by 4 per cent in the visual cortex of rats and decreased by 21 per cent in the superior colliculi. Other experiments with light deprivation showed similar results but were smaller in magnitude. Further results indicated that impairment in one sensory channel led to greater use of other modalities, *viz.,* blinded or light deprived animals raised in a complex environment showed increases in brain weight and AChE activity in the somesthetic area when compared with seeing animals in a comparable environment.

Diamond, Krech and Rosenzweig (1964) found that a complex environment led to histological changes in the rat cerebral cortex: the depth of the cortex increased and the number of cells per field decreased. The changes were more marked in the visual area than in the somesthetic area. The neurons, glia, and capillaries were less numerous in the animals exposed to the enriched environment, indicating a greater amount of intercellular and intervascular substance. They suggested that increased dendritic branching accounted for some of this substance. They reported also that the complex environment animals had more larger blood vessels and fewer smaller ones than isolated control animals.

It is an interesting fact that this group began with a search for chemical correlates of behavior (and have found them consistently) but it appears that their most significant results are those showing anatomical effects of experience.

Other individuals have found similar neuroanatomical changes. Altman (1966) reported that enriched experience animals showed greater volume and weight of cortex than did restricted environment animals. There was a greater uptake of radioactive isotope (suggesting greater activity) in the cortex of the enriched group as well.

Acetylcholine aspects have been related to behavior by other individuals. Takahashi and Aprison (1964) developed a near-freezing procedure which allowed them to obtain reliable estimates of the ACh content of various areas of the brain. Most investigators agree that freezing with liquid nitrogen is the best means of preserving ACh levels. If the usual decapitation technique is used, ACh levels can change during preparation of the tissue for analysis. They found that immersion in liquid nitrogen for a short time period (varying with different animals), decapitation and placement of the head in a cold chamber maintained at

0° C rapidly brought brain temperatures to 0°. For a rat, 9.5 seconds was the effective time period for immersion in liquid nitrogen. They reported the following ACh concentrations (M μ moles/g) in rat brain: telencephalon, 16.9; diencephalon, 22.3; caudate nucleus, 37.5; mesencephalon, 16.7; lower brain stem, 12.3; cerebellum, 2.3; olfactory bulb, 16.4; grey matter, 7.8; and white matter, 3.3. The grey and white matter were taken from the forebrain. It is interesting to note the low amounts of ACh in the cerebellum. Nucleic acid indices of functional activity (see Chapter 8) also indicate low activity in the cerebellum.

Takahashi and Aprison showed that during convulsions induced by Metrazol, significant decreases in ACh content (approximately 44 per cent) in the rat brain occurred with the near freezing and complete freezing methods. If the animal was decapitated before immersion in liquid nitrogen a decrement of 2.6 per cent resulted. Work to be discussed in Chapter 8 shows decrement in RNA during convulsions. Based on these results, plus logical considerations, one should expect some relationship between ACh and RNA during activity.

Mitchell (1963) showed that if a saline solution in a cup was placed on the surface of the cerebral cortex, ACh would diffuse from the cortex into the solution. He found that under chloralose anesthesia ACh output decreased; ACh output of the somesthetic cortex increased during afferent stimulation. Kanai and Szerb (1965) found that ACh output from the cortex of anesthetized cats increased five to six times during stimulation of the mesencephalic reticular activating system. Stimulation of the contralateral forepaw increased ACh output mainly from the somesthetic area.

In a review of a number of studies, Quastel (1962) indicated that the total ACh content of rat and mice brains depended on the physiological state of the animal. It varied inversely with activity level, increasing during sleep and anesthesia and decreasing in emotional states, convulsions, or electrical stimulations.

Two major difficulties are posed for proponents of this chemical approach. The central thesis of Krech and his associates, and others, is that the chemicals being measured operate at the synapse. Their techniques are not refined enough to indicate conclusively that this is so. Thus, the ACh-AChE activity could be more diffuse. However, a number of electron microscopy studies have shown that small vesicles are located in the presynaptic ending. The vesicles are supposed to contain packets of ACh. Furthermore, de Robertis *et al.* (1962, 1963*a,* 1963*b*) have isolated synaptic vesicles from brain cortex of rats. They reported that ACh and ChA (choline acetylase, the enzyme involved in the synthesis of ACh) were contained in synaptic vesicles but that AChE was probably localized at the membranes of the nerve endings. These evidences would be consistent with the hypotheses. Yet the idea that ACh is the main synaptic transmitter substance in the brain is still controversial (Ochs, 1965).

The second difficulty is one that confronted the Hebbian system (Hebb, 1949). Milner (1957) indicated that a deficiency of the Hebbian system was its emphasis on neural excitation to the exclusion of inhibitory phenomena and maintained that these latter events could not be explained by lack of facilitation. Hence, he introduced an active mechanism for inhibition involving an interaction between cells. The same criticism can be leveled at the synaptic chemical approach. Both approaches appear to be handling inhibitory phenomena as a lack of facilitation; however, inhibition could be handled by suggesting regulatory chemicals such as GABA.

An important question relates to the exact role of ACh and AChE in learning and other behavior. It appears probable that their function is the same in all behavior, a secondary one of facilitating the transmission of nerve impulses so that other neurochemical events can occur intra and intercellularly.

Intracellular Molecular Approach

This approach (the molecular psychobiological one) is the concern of later chapters. At this point, however, it would be worthwhile to discuss early work in this area.

Up to approximately fifteen years ago protein molecules were considered to be the substance of the genes. Protein was the favorite candidate also for being involved in the memory trace (Katz and Halstead, 1950; Halstead, 1951; Gerard, 1953). Although a number of individuals suggested the possible involvement of proteins in memory, the first systematic set of hypotheses was by Halstead. Katz and Halstead (1950) and Halstead (1951) suggested that nucleoproteins were the substances which had the ability to act as templates on which replica molecules were formed. At first the neurons of the brain were supposed to contain random configurations of protein. Stimulation of neural tissue by impulses caused the randomly oriented molecules to assume a specific configuration. Nucleoproteins were involved in these reorientations and became templates. They believed that these templates are like those of the germ cells in representing native endowment but differ from the latter in arising from external stimulation. They stated that the ordering of the protein templates could take place in various components of the cell and its processes, including the synapse. However, the reorganized protein replicas ultimately reside in the neural membranes where they participate as "traces."

These hypotheses stimulated some interest among scientists but the possibilities of the suggested model were not recognized at that time. Apparently the Zeitgeist was not ready for these ideas. However, in the intervening years with the important biological discoveries relative to the nucleic acids, the attention of psychologists and other behavioral scientists have been again directed to the molecular level.

If one substitutes the current molecular favorites, DNA or RNA, for the protein in the Halstead hypothesis, he sees that some of the current molecular hypotheses are similar, if not identical, to those of Halstead. Thus is is evident that Halstead cogently anticipated the current thought. We wonder if the Zeitgeist is now ready for this approach. Only time (and research efforts) will tell!

SECTION II
BEHAVIOR: GENETICS

CHAPTER 4

MOLECULAR BIOLOGY

SCOPE

Molecular biology is the broad discipline which is concerned with the molecular structures and functions of biological organisms. It comprises or overlaps with a large portion of the present day biological science, e.g., genetics, bacteriology, biochemistry, biophysics, histology, cytology and virology. Because its main concern has been with the nucleic acids, virology has contributed greatly to the development of molecular biology. In fact the major advances in this important area have been those of the virologists. Because viruses are relatively simple organisms, much work has been devoted to their structure and function, and these studies have led to great advances in understanding the structure and function of the nucleic acids.

A few years ago the favorite organism for many researchers was *Drosophilia*, the fruit fly. Studies with this animal provided much valuable information. In recent years *Drosophilia* has been replaced with bacteriophages (viruses which infest bacteria) and have led to a revolution in biology. Some individuals have maintained that the information uncovered in biology since 1950 has been as great, or greater than, all the information obtained prior to that year. This result is mainly due to the studies of bacteriophages and other viruses infecting plant and animal tissues. However, there is some suggestion that the insects may become favored animals again. The insect chromosomes in some tissues are large such that chromosomal "puffing" of gene sites can be observed microscopically. This puffing represents an expansion of certain DNA sites along the chromosome and is related to DNA activity. Attending puffings are developmental changes with RNA and protein synthesis. The puffing can be induced and thus the insect offers great possibilities for understanding the chemical changes underlying developmental events.

Many individuals in the behavioral sciences have confused

biochemistry and molecular biology. The latter is the broader of the two. Biochemistry is important in molecular biology in two ways: in understanding the biochemistry of the organism and in the biochemical methods which are required to extract the substances of concern. Biochemistry appears to be the fundamental sceince in present day biology. Thus the molecular biologist must be skilled in biochemistry.

Even the area of major concern for this book, molecular psychobiology, can be considered a sub-area of molecular biology. It involves the extension of molecular biology methods and concepts to behavioral problems such as learning.

SOME HISTORICAL DEVELOPMENTS

Potter (1960) has presented a concise historical introduction to the nucleic acids. This section will follow somewhat his survey.

The nucleic acids were discovered by Friedrich Miescher in 1869. His source material was discarded surgical bandages which were loaded with pus cells. Miescher digested the pus cells and obtained the nuclei. He extracted material from the nucleus which was called "nuclein" — this component was later named DNA. Later individuals were able to separate the purine and pyrimidine bases but it was to be approximately three quarters of a century before the significance of Miescher's discovery was evident. It was known that the nucleic acids were constructed from simpler units containing purines, pyrimidines, carbohydrates and phosphates, but many years of difficult research was to elapse before the structure of the nucleic acids was to be determined.

Most of the early work on the nucleic acids was conducted with thymus nucleic acid, which contained thymine and with yeast nucleic acid, which yielded uracil; adenine, guanine and cytosine were common to both. This led to the suggestion that animal cells contained the nucleic acid which today is called DNA whereas RNA was in plant cells. Furthermore, it was considered that the nucleic acids were contained only in the nucleus.

The present day conception that DNA is in both animal and plant nuclei and that RNA is located in both nucleus and cytoplasm of plant and animal cells was effected by the histochemical studies of Brachet beginning about 1933 in which ribonuclease (RNase) was used to break down and solubilize the RNA in cells and by the spectrophotometric studies of Caspersonn beginning about 1936.

After the constituents of the nucleic acids were determined, the important question was the mode of linkage. The basic unit was the mononucleotide, consisting of a nitrogenous base (purine or pyrimidine) attached to a pentose sugar which in turn was attached to a phosphate. Since the analytical data of the 1930's indicated approximately equal amounts of the four bases, the "tetranucleotide theory" was proposed, i.e., the nucleic acids consisted of repeating tetranucleotides with each of the four bases represented once in each repeating unit. A main reason for this theory was that *Escherichia coli* was used for many of the studies. *E. coli* is a bacterium which infests the gastrointestinal tract of humans and its DNA structure consists of approximately equal amounts of adenine, guanine, thymine and cytosine. Although the theory was never supported by evidence, the lack of contradictory evidence caused the idea to become widespread and reigned supreme. The death of this theory awaited improved techniques which developed during the 40's and 50's.

The modern era for nucleic acids was ushered in quite suddenly and unexpectedly by Avery, MacLeod and McCarty in 1944 when they showed that DNA extracted from one type of bacteria could be taken up by, and transform the characteristics of, a second type of bacteria. Protein had been considered the genetic material and many individuals argued that the DNA must have been contaminated with protein. But this report on the transforming ability of DNA raised questions concerning the adequacy of the tetranucleotide theory and provided greater impetus to the demand for an understanding of nucleic acid structure and function.

In the following two decades important techniques were developed to facilitate the task of understanding the nucleic acids. Schmidt and Thannhauser separated RNA and DNA chemically; Vischer and Chargaff separated nucleic acid components by paper chromatography; Cohn separated nucleic acids with column chromatography; Kornberg synthesized DNA with deoxyriboside triphosphates using a soluble enzyme from *E. coli;* Schwett, Lamfrom and Allen showed that proteins could be synthesized in a cell-free system; Kornberg and his colleagues developed the nearest neighbor technique, providing reliable information concerning dinucleotide sequences and showing that even though some species contained the same amounts of the four bases as did other unrelated species, the dinucleotide sequences were different; autoradiography and other labelling procedures were developed; Spiegelman, Bolton, McCarthy and others developed hybridization procedures; and Ochoa, Nirenberg and others were able to develop tentative codes for the amino acids in a peptide or protein chain using coding units of three nucleotides.

This last result is of profound importance but is also of interest in relation to the old tetranucleotide theory. The previous emphasis had been on four bases with their constituents repeating as a unit. Thus the tetranucleotide theory is replaced by a trinucleotide theory; however, the three nucleotides for a triplet are not the same for all of the coding triplets as was the case with the tetranucleotide theory.

A number of theoretical developments were of great significance. Chargaff noted in a variety of DNA preparations that the amount of adenine and thymine were approximately equal as was the amounts of guanine and cytosine. This was one piece of information which aided Watson and Crick in formulating their monumental description of the DNA structure as a double helix. The Watson-Crick contribution was one of the greatest to science and has influenced the thinking of all biologists to some degree. Another major theoretical contribution was that by Jacob and Monod in which they discussed the regulator, operator and structural genes conception and provided the groundwork for the messenger RNA concept which is so essential to present molecular biological ideas.

CHAPTER 5

STRUCTURE OF NUCLEIC ACIDS

PRIMARY AND SECONDARY STRUCTURE

D NA IS EXTREMELY thin, about 20 angstroms (Å) in diameter but very long, up to several millimeters. The strands of DNA in a single human cell would reach nearly six feet if stretched to full length. This amounts to some 10,000,000,000 miles of DNA in every man and woman; Stanley and Valens (1961) suggested that

Figure 5-1. Two-stranded DNA molecule in helical form.

in humans there are 800,000 DNA molecules each with about 40,000 nucleotides, or about 32 billion nucleotides in all. Other estimates (Tatum, 1964) have been lower, however, only 5 billion nucleotides. In the rat an estimate of 750,000 DNA molecules each with about 15,000 nucleotides, has been provided. DNA is a large double strand molecule which is wound in a helix (like a spiral staircase) and is found in the nucleus of cells (Fig. 5-1). Each strand is a complement of the other and has recurring patterns of constituents throughout its length, called nucleotides. A nucleotide consists of a phosphate attached to a sugar-base linkage; the DNA nucleotide, deoxyadenylic acid, is shown in Figure 5-2. The sugar attached to a base is called a nucleoside. The nucleoside resulting from removal of the phosphate in Figure 5-2 would be deoxyadenosine. Figure 5-3 indicates a portion of a DNA molecule as it would appear if it were unwound from its helical formation. The nucleoside of one strand is bonded to its corresponding part of the other strand by hydrogen bonds.

The bases consist of two types: purines and pyrimidines. There are two purines, adenine (A) and guanine (G), and two pyrimidines, thymine (T) and cytosine (C). The purines are larger molecules than are the pyrimidines. At the sugar-base points of the strands, a purine of one strand is always attached to a pyrimidine. Two purines are too big to bridge the gap between the two strands and two pyrimidines are too small. Furthermore, the amounts of A and T are always equal and the amounts of G and C are equal also; A is always paired with T and G with C. Thus there are two basic pairings as shown in Figure 5-4. The triple bonding between G and C is stronger than the double H bonding of A and T. These pairings could be considered a two unit code similar to the dot-dash Morse Code. However, if we consider the order of the bases in a single strand, there are four basic types of nucleotides. The four bases provide an alphabet of four symbols.

The sequence of the bases furnish the basis for the "codes" of genetic potential inasmuch as the main differences between DNA molecules appears to be the sequence of these bases. Even though there are only four possible nucleotides, the strands of the mole-

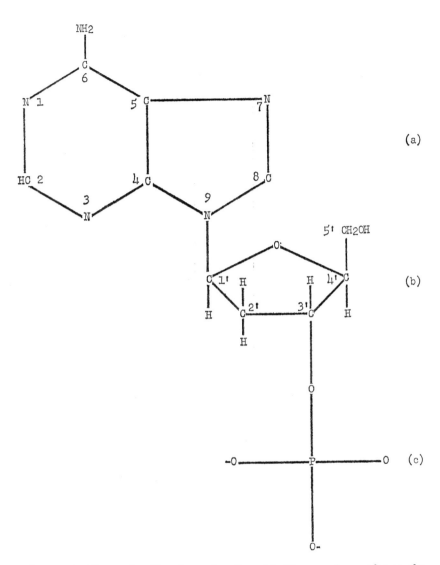

Figure 5-2. The nucleotide, deoxyadenylic acid. The numbers refer to the carbon positions and are used for identification purposes. (a) is the purine base adenine; (b) deoxyribose sugar; (c) phosphate.

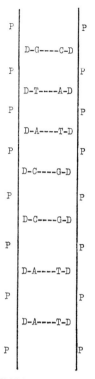

Figure 5-3. A portion of the DNA molecule as it would appear if unwound from its helical formation. P, is phosphate; D, deoxyribose; A, adenine; T, thymine; C, cytosine; and G, guanine.

cule are extremely long and allow for many possibilities. DNA molecules consist of thousands of units. But let us be conservative and assume that only 1,000 units are present in a single DNA molecule, a figure which is much less than that which occurs even in the smallest virus. In this case the number of possibilities is $4^{1,000}$, assuming independence of sites. These figures are tremendous. However, when we consider the number of possibilities for the many DNA in the chromosomes, the possibilities are incomprehensible. Thus it is obvious why biological scientists believe that these sugar-base attachments may furnish the "language" of the genes. Crick (1954, 1957) has stated that there is enough DNA in a single cell of the human body to encode about 1,000 large textbooks.

RNA molecules are similar to DNA but contain uracil (U) rather than T and ribose sugar rather than deoxyribose sugar. Ribose has an OH group (hydroxyl) at Carbon 2 whereas deoxyribose has only an H atom there; thus deoxyribose is less an oxygen as the name indicates. Another important aspect is that RNA is a single-stranded molecule although some RNA's contain loops in which bases bond to nearby bases to give the appearance of double strand molecular structure. The names of the bases,

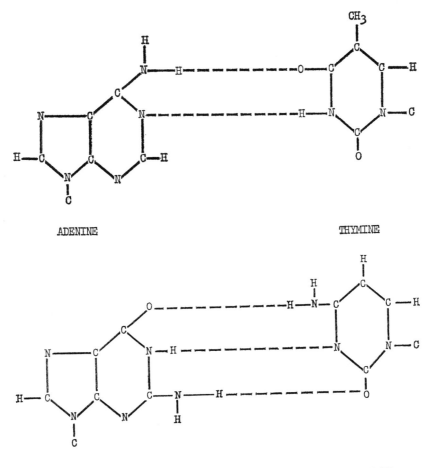

Figure 5-4. The bases present in DNA. RNA is similar except that uracil replaces thymine, and ribose sugar replaces deoxyribose sugar. C is carbon; N, nitrogen; H, hydrogen; and O, oxygen.

nucleosides and nucleotides of RNA and DNA are given in Table
5-I. The diameter of RNA molecules is 10 to 15 Å; their length is
up to several thousand angstroms.

TABLE 5-I
BASES, NUCLEOSIDES, AND NUCLEOTIDES OF THE NUCLEIC ACIDS

	Base	Nucleoside	Nucleotide
DNA	adenine	deoxyadenosine	deoxyadenylic acid
	guanine	deoxyguanosine	deoxyguanylic acid
	cytosine	deoxycytidine	deoxycytidylic acid
	thymine	thymidine	thymidylic acid
RNA	adenine	adenosine	adenylic acid
	guanine	guanosine	guanylic acid
	cytosine	cytidine	cytidylic acid
	uracil	uridine	uridylic acid

RNA is found in the nucleus and in the cytoplasm (approximately 10 and 90 per cent respectively) with the RNA in the
nucleus the most active; ribosomal RNA shows great stability as
does DNA. Some individuals have reported six RNA fractions:
chromosomal RNA, nucleoplasmic RNA, two fractions in the
nucleolus (one of which is "messenger" RNA) and ribosomal and
transfer RNA in the cytoplasm. However, it is probable that there
are only three RNA fractions which are synthesized by DNA in
the nucleus and then proceed to the cytoplasm: messenger RNA,
transfer or soluble RNA and ribosomal RNA.* Particles in the
nucleolus bear at least a superficial resemblance to ribosomal
particles (Swift, 1962). Recently, Chipchase and Birnstiel (1963)
have used a DNA-RNA hybridization procedure (see Appendix
A) to show that nucleolar RNA is identical to ribosomal RNA in
base sequence and that the DNA regions complementary to ribosomal RNA were not confined to the nucleolus but were scattered
throughout the nucleus and comprise approximately .30 per cent
of the total DNA sites. Perry, Srinvasan and Kelley (1964) have
found also that nucleolar RNA appears to be the precursor of
ribosomal RNA. Using radioactive labeling, Comb, Brown and
Katz (1964) found that the nucleolus was the site of ribosomal
RNA synthesis whereas the chromatin was the site for messenger
RNA synthesis.

---

*Bonner (1965) found a fourth type of RNA adhering to histones, apparently pro-
viding a specificity for the latter's complexing with DNA.

Jacob and Monod (1961) introduced the concept of messenger RNA. The characteristics which are included in the definition of this RNA fraction are the following (Jacob and Monod, 1961; Grunberg-Manago, 1963) :

1) It has a base composition reflecting the DNA base composition and has long base sequences which are complementary to its homologous DNA.
2) It is heterogeneous in molecular weights which reflects the different sizes of the protein chains to be synthesized.
3) It is associated with ribosomes during protein synthesis.
4) Its turnover is very high, i.e., it is short lived.
5) It stimulates protein synthesis (*in vivo* and in a cell free system).

Although one might consider that (1) was the characteristic most useful in differentiating messenger RNA from transfer and ribosomal RNA's, this is not so. In that studies suggest that all RNA is synthesized by DNA sites, each RNA molecule would have to satisfy condition (1). One possible exception may be transfer RNA which is assumed to be synthesized in the nucleus by DNA but has nucleotides added in the cytoplasm.

Characteristic (4) is a useful one for differentiation purposes, although some long lived messenger RNA's have been reported, e.g., in ocular lens and feather cells of chicks (Scott and Bell, 1964).

Characteristic (5) is the basic one for the messenger concept and is the most useful for differentiation purposes (Barondes *et al.*, 1962).

The notion of messenger RNA was developed from studies with bacteria. Recently it has been shown that this type of RNA is also present in mammalian cells (e.g., Barondes *et al.*, 1962; Scott and Bell, 1964; Sonneborn, 1964).

Ribosomes are about 200Å in diameter and consist of about half protein and the other half RNA; in general the RNA varies from 30 to 65 per cent depending on the species involved (Grunberg-Manago, 1963). Ribosomes in goat brain cortex have been indicated to contain 30 per cent RNA and 70 per cent protein and differed from similar preparations from the liver (Datta and

Ghosh, 1964). The ribosomal structure is strongly dependent on the amount of magnesium present in the medium. If magnesium is not present, the large particle breaks down to smaller ones. In bacteria the ribosomes probably exist as 100 S (Svedberg unit based on rate of sedimentation) or 70 S particles but can dissociate to 50S and 30S particles (Loewy and Siekevitz, 1963). The 30S particles contain one molecule of 16S RNA and about 10 molecules of protein while 50S particles have either one 23S or two 16S molecules and 20 molecules of protein with the RNA appearing to be on the surface of the ribosome (Santer, 1962). In yeast and mammalian cells the ribosomes probably exist as 120S and 80S particles. These can be split to 60S and 40S particles. The proteins of the ribosomes seem to be somewhat the same kind as the histones which are found in the nucleus. The base composition of the 30S, 50S, and 70S RNA particles in *E. coli* is roughly the same (Grunberg-Manago, 1963).

X-ray diffraction studies of *E. coli* ribosomes have indicated that the substructure consists of linear aggregates of particles and that the RNA and protein components are somewhat independent (Langridge, 1963). Detailed analyses suggested that an array of four or five parallel RNA double helices, 45 to 50Å apart, were involved; the protein component might fulfill a structural function in preserving the spacing in the parallel RNA, perhaps interacting with the RNA in the non-helical regions. The 45 to 50Å spacing was common to ribosomes from *E. coli, Drosophilia* larvae, rat liver and rat reticulocyte.

Transfer RNA is the smallest of the nucleic acids, containing 50 to 100 base units with a length of approximately 250 Å when unfolded. There are a number of different transfer RNA's; each one appears to be a single strand looped molecule (like a twisted hair pin) with profuse base pairing in the loops. It terminates in the sequence CCA at one end and G at the other end. There is evidence that in most samples the fourth nucleotide, next to cytidylic acid, is either an A or G nucleotide (Smellie, 1963). The fourth nucleotide contains A in 69 per cent of *E. coli* RNA and in most of the rat liver RNA (Grunberg-Manago, 1963). The trinucleotide portion which is specific for messenger RNA pairing (see

Chapter 6) is presumed to be located in the central part of the molecule (Nirenberg, 1963; Wilkins, 1963). Zubay (1963) has utilized the available physical-chemical data to develop a molecular model of transfer RNA with 67 bases (Fig. 5-5). The folded portion with secondary helical structure consists of thirty base pairs and encompasses about three turns of the helix. Of the seven remaining bases, only five are unpaired; the G at one end and the innermost C of the other end pair through a hydrogen bond.

Recently Holley *et al.* (1965) were able to purify three transfer RNA's from yeast which were specific for alanine, tyrosine and valine respectively. They established that the nucleotide sequences of each were different by careful analyses of the breakdown products following RNase treatment. At this time they have determined the complete nucleotide sequence of the alanine transfer RNA and are attempting to do the same for the tyrosine and valine RNA's. The alanine transfer RNA contained 77 nucleotides.

Figure 5-5. A conception of the structure of a transfer RNA. Base-pairings are assumed to occur in each of the three loops.

This marvelous achievement of determining the nucleotide sequence of an RNA molecule reveals for the first time the complete primary structure of a gene (Sonneborn, 1965). Transfer RNA's are coded by certain DNA sites and the linear sequence of bases in these RNA's are complementary to those in DNA. Thus knowing the complete sequence of bases in the alanine transfer RNA allows one to determine the DNA sequence which is responsible for this RNA.

It seems probable that transfer RNA is synthesized in the nucleus and proceeds to the cytoplasm where it has the CCA terminal sequence added because the enzymes responsible for this addition appear to be located in the cytoplasm (Smellie, 1963).

An interesting observation concerning transfer RNA is that it contains a number of unusual bases: pseudouracil, thymine, 2-methyladenine, 6-methylamino-purine and 1-methylguanine, as well as others; the exact function of these bases is unknown (Srinvason and Borek, 1964). Ribosomal RNA contains some of these odd bases also; however, since transfer RNA is considered to interact with ribosomes, bearing amino acids (see Chapter 6), it is possible that some of these bases are trapped in the ribosomes. The enzymes, RNA methylases, whose apparent function is the introduction of methyl groups (CH_3) on transfer RNA, are concentrated in the nucleolus which suggests that the methylation of transfer RNA occurs here (Birnstiel, Fleissner and Borek, 1963), although other evidence suggests the methylation occurs in the cytoplasm (Comb and Katz, 1964). The base composition of transfer RNA differs from that of both ribosomal RNA and DNA (Grunberg-Manago, 1963). Nuclear RNA differs from cytoplasmic RNA; in guinea pig brains, the nuclear RNA contains significantly greater amounts of uracil and less guanine than do other subcellular fractions (Yamagami, Kawakita and Naka, 1964).

Using ingenious procedures, molecular biologists have been able to get estimates in bacteria of the percentage of total DNA which synthesizes ribosomal and transfer RNA. Even though ribosomal RNA comprises up to 80 to 90 per cent of the total RNA in the cell, Yankofsky and Spiegelman (1963) and Chipchase and Birnstiel (1963) have indicated that about .30 per cent of total DNA sites is involved in its synthesis. Likewise, Goodman and Rich (1962) have found that .025 per cent of DNA synthesizes transfer RNA. Thus the synthesis of both these RNA's is determined by less than one percent of the total DNA in bacteria. The synthesis of messenger RNA would involve large portions of the DNA sites; however, less than the remaining 99-plus per cent of DNA would appear to have this function because DNA's operate for other than protein synthesis events. Current thought in genetics is that there are three types of genes (or DNA): structural genes, regulator genes and operator genes. Only the first is involved in the direct synthesis of RNA's for protein synthesis; the remaining two regulate the rate of protein synthesis.

The above description is relative to the primary and secondary structure of the nucleic acids, i.e., the linear sequence of bases (primary) and the H bonding across helices (secondary).

Secondary structure is expressed in DNA by the hydrogen bonding between bases on the two strands. Most RNA's which are of single strand nature, have secondary structure with profuse bonding presumed to occur throughout the helical portions. Both transfer RNA and ribosomal RNA have secondary structure; messenger RNA does not, however; secondary structure appears to interfere with its biological activity (Nirenberg, 1963, 1964).

EXCEPTIONS

The above description of primary and secondary structure is in terms of what usually occurs. There are, however, a number of exceptions which should be considered.

1) Deoxyribose (a five carbon or pentose sugar) is in DNA molecules. However, in a few bacteriophages glucose (a six carbon or hexose sugar) is found, e.g., T2, T4 and T6.

2) Although not a normal base, uracil has been reported in DNA (Belozersky and Spirin, 1960).

3) Likewise, thymine has been found in RNA, e.g., in transfer RNA, in wheat germ, in *E. coli* and other bacteria (Belozersky and Spirin, 1960).

4) The DNA in T2, T4 and T6 (bacteriophages which infest *E. coli*) have 5-hydroxymethyl-cytosine in place of cytosine. The former contains both OH and CH_3 groups at carbon 5.

5) The information contained in the second strand of DNA

must be redundant in terms of information content because single strand DNA viruses have been found, e.g., øX
174 and S 13.

6) Most organisms contain DNA which performs the genetic
function. Some viruses, however, contain only RNA which
is the genetic material. Those with RNA include polio,
influenza, and tobacco mosaic viruses.

7) Some viruses have double stranded RNA. For example,
reoviruses which inhabit the respiratory and enteric tracts
of man and animals have a highly ordered double stranded
helix (Gomatos and Tamm, 1963).

8) Extranuclear DNA has been reported in mitochondria of
both plants and animals and in plastids (operative for
photosynthesis) of plant cells (Gibor and Granick, 1964;
Granick, 1965).

TERTIARY STRUCTURE

Tertiary structure is concerned with the overall configuration
of the molecules; the nucleic acids can exist in a number of configurations. For example, DNA's vary in the number of base pairs
per turn of helix and in the inclination of the base pairs in the
molecule (Wilkins, 1963). Both nucleic acids vary their configurations somewhat with some changes in the chemical environment. DNA is a relatively rigid rod in its natural state. Upon
denaturation both nucleic acids form random coils.

QUATERNARY STRUCTURE

The three structures relate to the characteristics of single
molecules. However, quaternary structure refers to the interaction
or complexing of a nucleic acid with other nucleic acids or proteins or other molecules. There are two types of quaternary structures which are of significance to this book.

It has been indicated that the presence of certain chemicals
within an organism can later lead to an increase in the amounts of
specific enzymes available. This is called enzyme induction. The
specific mechanism which has been suggested for this event is that
a regulator gene (DNA) produces a repressor substance consisting
of an RNA, or an RNA and protein (Jacob and Monod, 1961;

Platt, 1962; Sypherd and Strauss, 1963). If a corepressor (possibly excessive amounts of a chemical) complexes with the repressor substance, the complex interacts with other DNA (operator gene sites). This process inhibits the functioning of structural genes in making messenger RNA for the synthesis of a specific protein. The overall result is complete cessation of, or a slow down in, production of the specific protein. If the repressor substance complexes with an inducer, the interaction with the operator gene leads to an increased production of the protein. Results which suggest such repression and induction at the gene level have been obtained by Hayashi *et al.* (1963).

Pardee (1962) suggested that genes or ribosomes could be the site of attachment for the repressor substance. He indicated that the ribosome was the most popular candidate because of the ease in visualizing the repressor as blocking the laying down of amino acids on the template or preventing the release of the finished enzyme. In line with this suggestion are the recent results of Hoagland *et al.* (1964). They reported inhibition of protein synthesis by a component which appeared to be in the membranous portion of the microsome. The inhibition was reversed by guanosine triphosphate (GTP); there was a direct proportionality between inhibitor concentration and degree of GTP stimulation. They suggested that GTP played a role in normal regulatory processes. Ohtaka and Spiegelman (1963) also reported results showing regulation at the point of protein synthesis.

Thus it appears that mechanisms acting at the gene level and at the ribosomal level influence protein synthesis.

Hurwitz and August (1963) suggested that different species of transfer RNA act as repressors of RNA synthesis, and amino acids as inducers. Thus each specific repressor transfer RNA would be "neutralized" by a specific amino acid in the formation of an aminoacyl RNA compound.

A second quaternary mechanism involves the complexing of DNA with proteins. Proteins consist of a number of amino acid molecules joined together in a long chain, with side branchings. For example, insulin has fifty-one amino acid units. There are twenty common amino acids in nature, all of which contain one or more amine (NH_2) and carboxyl (COOH) groups. Two amino acids link together through the amine and carboxyl groups, with the release of one molecule of water (H from NH_2 and OH from COOH).

Stedman and Stedman (1950) had assigned an important function to the nuclear proteins, histones, that of controlling gene activity. A number of other individuals (e.g., Bonner, see Chapter 6) have suggested the same. Histones have a high content of basic amino acids (mainly arginine and lysine). They are a heterogeneous group of proteins; at present twelve to twenty histones are believed to be present in varying amounts in cells; however, the histones have been fractionated into four components with ethanol and hydrochloric acid treatment, followed by column chromatography. These fractions have been denoted as Fl (very lysine rich). F2a (lysine rich), F2b (lysine rich) and F3 (arginine rich). In calf thymus Fl contains 30 per cent lysine and 22 per cent alanine; F2a — 11 per cent lysine, 12 per cent arginine, 13 per cent glycine, 10 per cent alanine, and 10 per cent leucine; F2b — 16 per cent lysine, 8 per cent arginine, and 11 per cent alanine; and F3 — 10 per cent lysine, 13 per cent arginine, and 13 per cent alanine. In each fraction there were small amounts of other amino acids (Billen and Hnilica, 1964).

The histones tend to be intimately associated with DNA; when amounts of DNA increase, the amounts of histones do likewise. There are also acidic proteins in the nucleus. Their importance metabolically is evident from their high rates of turnover (Busch *et al.,* 1963). The acidic proteins and histones are approximately equal in amount, each comprising approximately 20-25 per cent of the total dry weight of the nucleus in the rat liver. Busch *et al.* (1963) have suggested that DNA and the acidic proteins compete for linkage with histones and that loss of histones from linkage with DNA to the acidic proteins would free DNA for synthesis functions.

Bloch (1963) has estimated that there are roughly four amino acids in histone molecules for every nucleotide in the associated DNA and that a given DNA unit is capable of associating with many histones.

Busch (1965) suggested that in a mammalian cell with approximately 700,000 DNA molecules of about 15,000 nucleotides, there could be about 250,000,000 histone molecules. This would result in one histone molecule for each 42 nucleotides.

Busch *et al.* (1964) investigated the incorporation of labeled amino acids into proteins of the four fractions in tumor and liver cells of rats. Their results suggested that the histones dissociate from DNA complexes and that about 50 per cent of the histones in the tumor would be synthesized every twenty-four hours but only 3-6 per cent of histones in the liver would be synthesized in the same time period.

An excellent treatment of histones is available in the recent books by Bonner and Ts'O (1964) and by Busch (1965).

INTERCELL STRUCTURAL DIFFERENCES

It is probable that the nucleic acids differ from cell to cell in important characteristics. Even though the same genetic information or potential is in every nucleus, the same information is not being expressed in every cell. Some regulatory mechanisms allow certain information to be expressed whereas other information is being repressed. The exact mechanisms are not known. However, the quaternary structures discussed above, e.g., DNA-histone complexing, may be important.

Dingman and Sporn (1962) have indicated that the RNA of the microsomes of rat brain does not differ from that in rat liver, but differences are present in nuclear RNA of the two tissues. Furthermore, the nuclear RNA of young rats was different than that of adult rats. They were not able to indicate whether the differences were in primary, secondary, or tertiary structure. To determine differences they used absorption characteristics, absorption spectrum following alkaline hydrolysis, resistance to RNase activity, absorbency following heating and optical rotation. In another study, they found that DNA-histone complexing was different in various cells. The proportion of histone complexed with DNA was greater in erythrocytes than it was in brain and liver (Sporn and Dingman, 1963).

CHROMOSOMAL STRUCTURE

Chromosomes consist of DNA, RNA and proteins. Evidence has indicated that DNA is the genetic material. Some of the RNA that has been reported in chromosomes may be newly synthesized strands but some RNA may perform a supportive role. The proteins presumably serve some supportive role also, although some proteins may serve a regulatory function.

There are two types of proteins in the chromosomes: non-histones and histones. The latter have received more attention because of their apparent inhibitory effect on RNA synthesis. That they function intimately with DNA is suggested by their close association and by the fact that the amounts of DNA and histones vary together. For example, in the RNA-rich chromosomal puffs in certain insects, the amounts of DNA and histones remain constant (Swift, 1962). In the DNA-rich puffs of the insect *Sciara* both histones and DNA increase in amount. Thus in both RNA and DNA puffs, histones follow the pattern of DNA.

On the other hand, the nonhistone proteins are not similar to the DNA distribution but are associated mainly with the RNA puffs.

The exact form that DNA and histones take in chromosomal material is not certain. It has been suggested that at least half of the histones bound to DNA are in helical formation and that DNA-histone extends the length of the chromosomal fiber. Some investigators have proposed that the histones are wound about the DNA double helix, lying in the groove (Sager and Ryan, 1961). Zubay (1964) suggested that histones form bridges between adjacent DNA molecules with the long axis of the helical histones at an angle of 60° to the long axis of the DNA molecules. He indicated that the bridges facilitate the supercoiling of DNA in a single chromosome. Before becoming active the supercoiled regions would unwind and the histone bridges broken and possibly reformed between less highly coiled filaments of DNA.

Electron micrographs show a diameter of 20 Å for DNA and 30 Å for DNA-histone whereas chromosomes have been observed in electron micrographs to be 100 Å in diameter. Ris (1964) reported that chromosomal threads in erythrocyte nuclei of the salamander were about 200 Å thick, probably representing two 100 Å fibrils. He thought that four parallel DNA strands and the histones associated with them comprised the 200 Å thread. He found similar threads in somatic nuclei of other tissues and also in plant nuclei, suggesting a general unit of organization of DNA-histones in chromosomes.

On the other hand, some individuals suggest that a linear array of single DNA molecules, rather than multiple, strands, are in the chromosome (Painter, 1964). The Zubay model of DNA-histone bridging would fit in this category.

It is also not certain whether DNA or protein forms the axis of the chromosome. Painter (1964) submitted a lot of evidence to show that protein usually forms the axis.

In spite of the different views toward chromosomal structure, it is certain that DNA is the genetic material within the chromosome. Treatment of chromosomes with DNase brings about a loss of genetic activity.

RELATED ASPECTS

One would expect that the amount of DNA should increase with increasing complexity of organisms. Rich (1962) has indicated that such is the case with a variety of organisms. However, even though there is trend in this direction, no great increase per cell is found in organisms (Table 5-II) from fish to man (Sager and Ryan, 1961).

TABLE 5-II
DNA CONTENT OF VARIOUS CELL TYPES
(from Sager and Ryan, 1961)

Organism	*Values in Picograms $= 10^{-12}$ Grams Per Nucleus*	
	Haploid	Diploid
Phage T4	2×10^{-4}	
E. coli	4×10^{-2}	
Yeast	4×10^{-2}	
Neurospora		
Aspergillus		
Drosophila		1.7×10^{-1}
Zea Mays		7
Mouse		5
Rat	1×10^{-2}	6.5 — 7.6
Beef Cattle	2.3×10^{-2}	6.4 — 6.8
Man	3.3	6.0 — 6.8
Domestic Fowl		2.4 — 2.6
Shad	1.3	1.99
Carp	0.91	3.0 — 3.3
Rainbow trout	1.6	4.9
Toad	2.45	7.3
Frog	3.7	15.0

Another interesting result is related to the heterogeneity of DNA base composition. Even though the mean amounts of G-C pairings vary approximately from 25 to 75 per cent in bacteria, the mean G-C content varies little in vertebrates, from approximately 40 to 44 per cent (Schildkraut, Marmur and Doty, 1962; Sueoka, 1961). The G-C content distribution of the DNA molecules of an organism is relatively narrow and generally unimodal. The variance for bacteria tends to be less than that of higher organisms. Both rats and humans have a mean G-C content of approximately 40 per cent. Presumably differences between man and rats are expressed not in base amounts but in the exact sequences of these bases. Table 5-III shows the amounts of the four DNA bases in different organs and species (Chargaff, 1955) and the A+T/G+C ratio. Notice that the percentages of bases are the same (within random variation) for tissues within the same species.

TABLE 5-III
THE DISTRIBUTION OF DNA BASES IN VARIOUS ORGANS AND SPECIES
(from Chargaff, 1955)

Organism	Organ	A	G	C	T	A+T/G+C
Ox	Thymus	29.0	21.2	21.2	28.5	1.36
	Liver	28.8	21.0	21.1	29.0	1.37
Sheep	Thymus	29.3	21.4	21.0	28.3	1.36
	Liver	29.3	20.7	20.8	29.2	1.41
Pig	Thymus	30.0	20.4	20.7	28.9	1.43
	Liver	29.4	20.5	20.5	29.7	1.44
	Spleen	29.6	20.4	20.8	29.2	1.43
	Thyroid	30.0	20.8	20.7	28.5	1.41
Man	Thymus	30.9	19.9	19.8	29.4	1.52
	Liver	30.3	19.5	19.9	30.3	1.54

A further expectation would be that the DNA of an organism should be related to its RNA. Belozersky and Spirin (1960) reported that the DNA ratio, A+T/G+C, over various species of bacteria, fungi, and algae varied from .35 to 2.70; however, the corresponding RNA ratio, A+U/G+C, over the same species deviated very little from 1.00. Sager and Ryan (1961) indicated that greater variation occurred in DNA ratios than in RNA ratios of other species as well. Thus there is little relationship between these ratios over species. This unexpected result was explained by suggesting that some RNA's are related to the DNA whereas others are irrelevant. Alternatively, one might suggest that only a portion of DNA is related to RNA. A direct relationship between RNA fractions (messenger RNA) and DNA has been reported in a number of experiments with bacteriophage and yeast (Hall and Spiegelman, 1961; Strauss, 1960) and in mammals. Likewise, there is obviously a direct relationship between the DNA sites which synthesize ribosomal RNA and this RNA; the same is true for the DNA-dependent transfer RNA synthesis. However, the DNA sites responsible for synthesizing the three RNA fractions must be much less than the total DNA sites available or greater DNA-RNA correlation should occur. This result (as well as other data) suggest that DNA functions in other events than protein synthesis.

CHAPTER 6

FUNCTION OF NUCLEIC ACIDS

GENETIC FUNCTION

I T HAS BEEN conclusively indicated that DNA carries the basic genetic material to determine whether an individual is to be a human, chimpanzee, rat, etc; whether he will have blue, brown, or other color eyes; whether he will tend to be large or small; etc. A number of sources of evidence have suggested that DNA is the genetic material but conclusive evidence was provided by the transformation experiments.

Indirect Evidence

If DNA performs the hereditary function, it should be located at gene sites and its quantity should be proportional to the number of genes. DNA is located only in the nucleus (with a few rare exceptions) where genetic material is found. Likewise, the content of DNA per cell nucleus is relatively constant. Furthermore, there is a relationship between the number of chromosome sets and amount of DNA (Strauss, 1960) as is indicated in Table 6-I. The haploid cells have approximately one half as much DNA as do diploid cells. In the liver there are tetraploid and octoploid cells which show approximately four times and eight times as much DNA as the haploid cell as one would expect if DNA were the genetic material.

There have been exceptions to the above statement with greater deviations from the expected DNA amounts; however, compared to the great changes that occur in the amount of RNA and protein, DNA appears relatively constant; thus the location and content of DNA are more closely correlated with the genes than are any other cellular components.

Another source of indirect evidence is the observation that DNA is metabolically inert and does not participate in cellular metabolism to the same extent as other cell components. This behavior would be expected of genetic material.

The fact that electron micrographs show that treatment of chromosomes with DNase, but not RNase or proteolytic agents, cause the chromosomal backbone to be broken lends further support to the notion.

Direct Evidence

The real evidence that shows DNA as the genetic material is furnished by the transformation experiments.

In 1944 Avery, MacLeod and McCarty extracted purified DNA from a bacterium, *Diplococcus pneumoniae,* of the smooth phenotype (Type III R). A small number of the latter were transformed to Type III S. However, if the DNA was treated with DNase, no transformation took place.

This result has been obtained by other researchers utilizing different bacteria. There is even a report of transformation in ducks (Butler, 1959). Other molecules, such as proteins, have no transforming ability. Thus it appears that DNA is endowed with genetic capability.

TABLE 6-I
DNA CONTENT IN MICROMICROGRAM PER NUCLEUS
OF DIPLOID AND HAPLOID CELLS
(after Vendrely, 1955)

Species	Diploid Erythrocyte	Liver	Haploid Sperm
Domestic fowl	2.34	2.39	1.26
Shad	1.97	2.01	0.91
Carp	3.49	3.33	1.64
Brown trout	5.79		2.67
Toad	7.33		3.70

DNA Duplication

Having shown evidence to indicate that DNA is the genetic material, one should be concerned with the manner in which the genetic potential encoded in the linear sequence of bases in DNA is transmitted in the developing embryo or in cells which are regenerating. This is the problem of DNA duplication.

It has been shown by experiments with *E. coli* that each of the two strands in DNA act as a separate template (Meselson and Stahl, 1958). They grew *E. coli* for several generations in a medium which contained N^{15}, a heavy nitrogen. The DNA from these bacteria is easily identified by cesium chloride density gradient centrifugation (see Appendix A) in that it is denser than normal DNA with N^{14}. Cells-containing N^{15} DNA was transferred to a medium that contained only N^{14}. They sampled the culture at various times, extracted DNA, and ascertained its density.

The sample times corresponded with the times of doubling of the cells within the culture. The first sample revealed DNA with an intermediate density which was interpreted as a hybrid DNA with one N^{15} strand and the other with an N^{14} strand. The second doubling of cells revealed two types of DNA in equal amounts, hybrid DNA and N^{14} DNA. A third sample gave the same amount of hybrid DNA as in the previous sample but there was three times as much N^{14} DNA. This experiment is represented in Figure 6-1.

These results suggest that DNA consists of a pair of templates complementary to each other, that in duplication the H bonds are broken, and that the two chains separate. Each chain acts as a template on which is formed a complementary chain so that two pairs of chains, four pairs, eight pairs, sixteen pairs, etc., eventuate where previously only one had been. These results are exactly those suggested by the Watson-Crick model.

Results identical to those of Meselson and Stahl have been obtained with other organisms. The DNA replication or synthesis requires the presence of an enzyme, DNA polymerase, to catalyse the reactions involved. Kornberg (1961) has synthesized DNA in a suitable medium including the polymerase and the nucleotide triphosphates.

PROTEIN SYNTHESIS

The interaction of DNA, RNA and amino acids in protein synthesis has been described frequently (Hurwitz and Furth, 1962; Ochoa, 1962; Rich, 1962). The basic information (genetic code) in DNA is transmitted to messenger RNA in the nucleus in the presence of an enzyme, RNA polymerase. The exact manner in which messenger RNA is manufactured is not known. There are two possibilities. First, the two-stranded DNA molecule

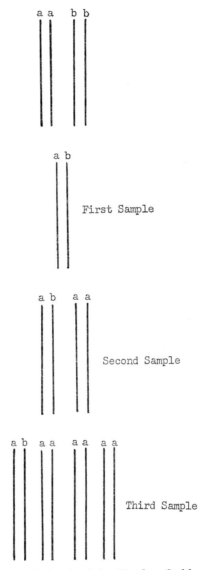

Figure 6-1. A diagrammatic sketch of the Meselson-Stahl experiment; a is N^{14} strand; b is N^{15} strand.

divides; one of these strands then forms a hybrid two-stranded molecule with messenger RNA which forms as a complement of the DNA. Thus if the one strand of DNA has the linear sequence ATTGC ...., messenger RNA would consist of UAACG .... The second possibility involves the RNA being synthesized as a third strand on DNA and then being released. *In vitro* studies indicate that each DNA strand synthesizes a messenger RNA whereas *in vivo* experiments suggest that only one strand is copied (Hurwitz and August, 1963; Hayashi, Hayashi and Spiegelman, 1963).

Messenger RNA is transferred from the nucleus to the ribosomes in the cytoplasm where it supervises the uniting of amino acids to form proteins (Fig. 6-2). The transfer of RNA from nucleus to cytoplasm can be demonstrated by radiographic techniques. However, some synthesis of proteins occurs also in the nucleus (Byrne, Levin, Bladen and Nirenberg, 1964; Birnstiel and Flamm, 1964; Reid and Cole, 1964). In the synthesis of protein, transfer RNA gathers an amino acid and attaches itself to its appropriate site on messenger RNA. There are supposed to be different transfer RNA's for each amino acid.

Thus many transfer RNA's with their associated amino acids "recognize" the appropriate site on messenger RNA and the amino acids become attached to form the specified protein. In this process it has been suggested by Warner, Rich and Hall (1962), based on electron microscopy, that a number of ribosomes (polysomes or polyribosomes) roll along a single messenger RNA like a ball, "reading" the message and attaching the amino acids in a polypeptide chain. Other experimental data tend to favor this suggestion (e.g., Hardesty, Miller and Schweet, 1963). The protein synthesized may form structural components for the organism or function as an enzyme. These latter proteins are extremely important in behavior.

Cannon, Krug and Gilbert (1963) found that the CCA end of transfer RNA molecules binds to the 50 S unit of the ribosome in *E. coli,* with only one molecule binding firmly. Their results did not exclude the possibility that there were other transfer

RNA-binding sites, however. Messenger RNA appears to bind to the 30 S particle (Sehon, 1965).

Warner and Rich (1964) reported results which implied that two transfer RNA's were attached to each ribosome which was active during protein synthesis whereas one was attached to in-

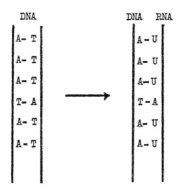

In Nucleus

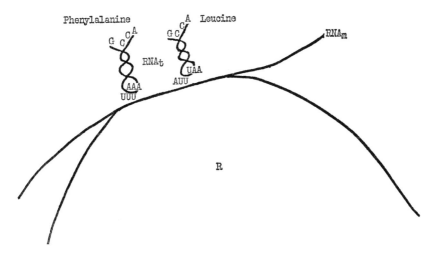

In Cytoplasm

Figure 6-2. A simplified diagram showing a portion of the DNA and RNA molecules involved in protein synthesis. RNA_m, messenger RNA; RNA_t, transfer RNA; R, ribosome.

active ribosomes. This work was done on the reticulocytes of rabbits. These cells manufacture a single protein, hemoglobin and thus have been convenient for the study of protein synthesis.

Henney and Storck (1964) found that polyribosomes were present in growing and germinating cells of *Neurospora crassa,* a fungus, but were not present in resting and dormant cells which were not synthesizing proteins, suggesting that polyribosomes are necessary for protein synthesis. Thus it appears that polyribosomes are included in growing cells which are involved in protein synthesis but are not present in nonactive cells because there are no messenger RNA's to hold the individual ribosomes together in a polyribosome unit.

If the synthesis of messenger RNA is prevented by actinomycin D, polyribosomes should disappear and be replaced by single ribosomes. Such effect has been indicated by Staehelin, Wettstein and Noll (1963) in rat liver.

If the DNA sites code for protein synthesis via the base sequences in RNA, an important question is "What is the size of the coding unit?" If the *codon* is by a single base, then there are 4^1 possible results corresponding to A, G, C and U. If a two letter code is involved, there are 4^2 or sixteen possibilities, AA, AG, AC, AU, GA, GG, etc. If a three letter code is offered, 4^3 or sixty-four different triplets result, AAA, AAG, AAC, etc. If a four letter code is required, 4^4 or 256 quadruplets occur; etc. Because there are twenty common amino acids in nature, a coding procedure of a minimum of three nucleotides for each amino acid has been considered to be most plausible (Crick, 1962; Crick *et al.,* 1961; Crick, 1963; Rich, 1962). Crick (1962) suggested that the message was read in nonoverlapping groups from a fixed point in groups of a fixed size that was probably three, although he did not rule out multiples of three, that there was very little nonsense in the code, and that in general more than one triplet could stand for each amino acid.

Matthaei *et al.* (1962) have developed tentative codes for most of the twenty amino acids by using synthetic polyribonucleotides to synthesize protein. For example, UUU represents phenylalanine; one U and two C's, proline, etc. The code is degenerate, i.e., more than one triplet can code for a single amino acid. For example, two U's and a C or a G is considered the code for leucine. Table 6-II gives the trinucleotide codes offered by a number of researchers. The table is a summary provided by Nirenberg (1963). Preliminary evidence has suggested that the code is somewhat universal with all species using the same code. For example, synthetic RNA polymers code the same way in a bacterial system as they do in mammalian cell free systems. However, some differences probably do occur. Because of the degeneracy of the code, it is probable that one species may use one of the alternate codes while another species uses a different one.

TABLE 6-II
TRINUCLEOTIDE CODING OF 20 COMMON
AMINO ACIDS (Sequence Arbitrary)
(from Nirenberg, 1963)

Amino Acid	Codes			
alanine	CCG	UGG		
arginine	CGC	AGA	UCG	
asparagine	ACA	AUA		
aspartic acid	GUA			
cysteine	UUG			
glutamic acid	GAA	AGU		
glutamine	ACA	AGA	AGU	
glycine	UGG	AGG		
histidine	ACC			
isoleucine	UAU	UAA		
leucine	UUG	UUC	UUA	UUU
lysine	AAA	AAG	AAU	
methionine	UGA			
phenylalanine	UUU			
proline	CCC	CCU	CCA	CCG
serine	UCU	UCC	UCG	
threonine	CAC	CAA		
tryptophan	GGU			
tryosine	AUU			
valine	UGU			

The coding results have been obtained by studying the process of protein synthesis in cell-free extracts of *E. coli* from the human colon (Nirenberg, 1963). The bacteria are grown rapidly in suitable nutrients and are harvested by sedimenting them by centrifugation. The cells are gently broken open by grinding them with a fine powder, releasing the cell sap which contains DNA, messenger RNA, ribosomes, enzymes and other components. These extracts are called cell-free systems and will incorporate amino acids into proteins when they are supplied with energy rich substances (mainly ATP — adenosine triphosphate). The incorporation process is followed by using amino acids containing radioactive carbon (C^{14}).

Even though trinucleotide coding is most accepted, other coding procedures have been suggested. Roberts (1962) indicated that a doublet code would eliminate degeneracy aspects. In this code, a G and a C represent alanine; a G and a U, valine; etc. However, this coding procedure results in ambiguities, e.g., AA codes lysine and methionine.

Several individuals favoured triplet codes which utilize certain doublet aspects. Eck (1963) discussed a symmetrical pattern for the sixty-four possible combinations of the four nucleotides taken three at a time. He suggested thirty-two pairs in which the second member of each pair was identical to the first except that in one position a purine is replaced by the other purine or a pyrimidine by the other pyrimidine. This symmetrical pattern was consistent with the reported triplet codes, allowed for prediction of amino acids corresponding to unidentified triplets, and suggested a structural basis for transfer RNA specificity. These triplets might facetiously be called a "two-and-a-half-letter" code in that one nucleotide could contain either of the purines (or either of the pyrimidines) and still be "recognized" by one transfer RNA. Thus there would be sixty-four possible triplets on messenger RNA but only thirty-two different transfer RNA's.

Jukes (1963) has suggested a "modified doublet" coding procedure which might be appropriately entitled a "greater than two but less than three letter" code. It was postulated that in each triplet there is a pivotal base which is subject to change without altering the coding function of the triplet. The pivotal base could not be in the third position nor could it be a G; it was U in eleven of the codes containing this base.

Certain recent observations have posed a problem for these genetic coding attempts. If synthetic RNA containing only uracil bases (poly U) is used as a template and is combined with ribosomes from *E. coli*, plus other necessary constituents, one would expect from the coding ideas that phenylalanine would be produced. However, phenylalanine incorporation is markedly dependent on magnesium ion concentration; when the concentration was increased, incorporation increased for amino acids (e.g., isoleucine) which were not normally "coded" for by poly U and incorporation of phenylalanine was reduced (Hechter and Halkerston, 1965). These results show the importance of internal environmental agents in protein synthesis.

An interesting "Book Model" of coding and genetic information transfer was proposed by Platt (1962). He used the analogy of a complex instruction manual in which "information" is linearly arranged in "words" that are "read out" sequentially in time. He related in a clever fashion the various aspects of books and printing procedures to the DNA, RNA and amino acid interaction.

A major question relative to this coding procedure is why fifty or more base units on a transfer RNA are required if a minimum of three base units on messenger RNA can code each amino acid. Presumably these extra base units are involved in the reaction in which the appropriate amino acid is activated and then attached to the transfer RNA.

MUTATIONS

If the linear sequence of bases in DNA provides the basis for genetic coding, one would expect that by changing the sequence at one or more sites mutation should occur. This has been indicated indirectly.

The base analogues have been used frequently in the DNA of bacteriophages to produce mutations. For example, 5-bromouracil and 2-aminopurine are presumed to act to bring about the replacement of the A-T pairs by G-C ones, and vice versa. These agents also bring about a reversion of these changes. Freese (1961) indicated that low pH, ethyl ethane sulfonate and other agents, will cause transitions from one pair to the other.

Benzer (1961, 1962) made a detailed examination of a small portion of the genetic map of bacteriophage T4, a portion which controls the ability of the phage to grow in *E. coli*. He indicated that A-T pairs are held much less strongly than are G-C pairs which suggests that in mutation the A-T pair "hot spots" will be more subject to substitution. He stated that A-T pairing would change to A-G and thereon to C-G.

Nitrous acid has been used as a mutagen with tobacco mosaic virus RNA. This reagent substitutes hydroxyl groups for amino groups. Nitrous acid reacts with nucleic acids containing A, G and C and converts them to the corresponding base analogues containing hydroxyl compounds, hypoxanthine, xanthine and U. These results imply that the reaction of nitrous acid with nucleic acids produces base analogues which result in mutation upon the duplication of genetic material. Tsugita and Fraenkel-Conrat (1960) showed that nitrous acid altered the composition of RNA of tobacco mosaic virus and that the resulting protein of the mutant differed from the parent strain with three amino acids being replaced by three other (proline, aspartic acid and threonine by leucine, alanine and serine).

REGULATORY FUNCTIONS

In the behavior of organisms there is need for some units to inhibit, control or regulate others so that organized behaviour will result. If no regulation were involved, behavior would be chaotic. At the gene level it has been suggested by Jacob and Monod (1961), and others, that regulator and operator DNA sites control the RNA synthesis of structural DNA sites and thereby the overall functional activity of the cells. (See Quaternary Structure in Chapter 5).

Busch, Starbuck, Singh and Ro (1964) suggested five genetic operating groups or polyoperons involved in cell functions. These are:

1) Basic cell metabolism.
2) A specialized cell function.
3) Cell growth.
4) Cell division.
5) Abnormal cell growth, e.g., cancer.

All cells of the organism would share in common the components of the first group which provides the basic elements necessary for the fundamental metabolism of the cell; however, the function for the other four would vary from cell to cell.

For regulation of these cell functions one would expect that some DNA's would be active whereas others would be inert. This appears to be the case. All cell nuclei contain the same genetic information but not all DNA sites can be active in synthesizing RNA. If all were active, cell differentiation would not occur and every cell would be the same. Thus two different types of DNA (in terms of functional activity) are to be expected.

Swift (1962) concluded from his studies on DNA in species of flies that there are two types of DNA: one which is constant from cell to cell and another varying in particular cell types at particular stages of ontogeny. Likewise, Bendich, Russell and Brown (1953) found two types of DNA in growing rat tissue, one showing greater amounts of turnover than the other. Sampson *et al.* (1963) reported two DNA fractions in plants; a high molecular weight stable fraction and a low molecular weight fraction showing a relatively rapid rate of turnover. The proportion of the two forms varied with physiological state and with the type of tissue. Male germinal tissue contained negligible amounts of the low molecular weight form. Growing regions of root and leaf had as much as 20 per cent of their total DNA in the low molecular weight form. Dormant embryos in wheat seeds had about 10 per cent, but the amount increased sharply on induction of germination.

Sampson *et al.* indicated that in respect to the properties investigated the high molecular weight stable form behaved typically for genetic material. However, the low molecular weight active DNA appeared to be performing a physiological role. Likewise, Frenster, Allfrey and Mirsky (1963) isolated active and repressed DNA fractions from interphase calf thymus lymphocyte chromatin.

Investigations of chromosomes of insects have shown puffing at specific chromosomal sites which are assumed to be sites of active DNA. These sites of activity appear to be at different loci in different tissue and at different loci in the same tissue at different times (Beermann and Clever, 1964). Karlson (1962) has reported that a hormone, ecdysone, is able to bring about puffing in the insect *Chironomus,* and soon thereafter the organism goes from the larva to the pupa state.

DNA activity is assumed to be highly cell specific (Markert, 1965) ; some genes function only in certain cells, and then only when the cell has reached a suitable stage in development. A good example is the gene for tyrosinase which is active only in the melanocyte at terminal stages of differentiation. This gene is present in other cells but is silent. A number of other examples can be cited: keratin is synthesized in epithelial cells, thyroglobulin in thyroid cells, actin and myosin in muscle cells, insulin in pancreatic islets, etc.

From these results there is the suggestion that DNA activity is governed by inhibitory or regulatory mechanisms. Such inhibition may be relaxed during cell differentiation and other cellular functions to allow some of the potential information to be expressed so that different cells can develop for different functions even though all cells contain the same potential information. Even the behavioral events of complex organisms such as man may involve a loosening of inhibitory mechanisms so that DNA activity with associated RNA synthesis may increase.

The enzyme induction event discussed in Chapter 5 is also pertinent here. In fact it was enzyme induction which led Jacob and Monod to formulate their regulator-operator-structural DNA model. The addition of an inducer such as thio-methyl-β-galactoside to a strain of *E. coli* stimulates the synthesis of the enzyme β-D-galactosidase. The genetic region responsible for utilization of β-galactoside in *E. coli* has been determined by involved genetic experiments. This region is referred to as the *lac* region. Hayashi, Spiegelman, Franklin and Luria (1963) added thio-methyl-β-D-galactoside to an *E. coli* medium and obtained increased amounts of β-galactosidase; they found also increased amounts of RNA which was complementary to the DNA of the *lac* region which supported the Jacob-Monod model of inducer action at the gene level. Other work (Pollard, 1964) indicated that the time of onset of enzyme activity after induction was about three minutes.

Kenney and Kull (1963) have found that hydrocortisone increases the rate of synthesis of liver nuclear RNA during the induction of tyrosine transaminase in adrenalectomized rats. Wicks and Kenny (1964) reported that testosterone injections in castrated rats resulted in a two to threefold increase in RNA synthesis in the seminal vesicle within fifty minutes after injection. Insulin led to an increase in messenger RNA and an increase in the specific activity of ribosomal RNA in rat diaphragm (Wool and Munro, 1963). Leslie (1955) and Brown and Roll (1955) reported increases in RNA and RNA/DNA ratios following the administration of various hormones. Olson (1964) found that actinomycin D inhibited vitamin K induced formation of prothrombin in chicks deficient in vitamin K; inhibition of RNA synthesis also occurred. He suggested that vitamin K and all fat-soluble vitamins operate to control the synthesis of specific proteins and enzymes. Other individuals (Karlson, 1962; Schneiderman and Gilbert, 1964) reported that hormones cause chromosomal puffing in insects, resulting in rapid RNA and protein synthesis in puffed regions. Bonner (personal communication) stated that there are at least twenty-two hormones which effect rapid RNA synthesis. The effect of a number of these on gene sites was discussed by Mechter and Halkerston (1965) and by Davidson (1965).

Histones complexed with DNA have been indicated to affect DNA activity (see Chapter 5). Huang and Bonner (1962) found with pea embryo chromatin that when the protein fraction, histone, was removed, the rate of RNA synthesis increased fivefold. Further work (Bonner and Huang, 1962a) showed that the chromatin contained 80 per cent DNA bound to histone and 20 per cent free DNA. They suggested that the function of histone was to bind DNA and block the transfer of "information" from DNA. Bonner and Huang (1962b) also discussed lack of inhibition following a reduction of histones in certain plants in transition from the vegetative to the flowering state. In these plants induction of flowering is brought about by exposure of a single leaf of the plant to a single long night. The leaf then sends a signal to the bud, the bud becomes transformed, and some forty-eight hours after the beginning of the long night,

histological, visible symptoms of floral differentiation begin to
make themselves apparent. It was shown that shortly after receiving the flowering message by the bud, and before any visible signs
of differentiation were apparent, a sharp drop in histone content
of the bud occurred. This was followed by a dramatic increase in
RNA concentration in the same cells.

Bonner and Huang (1964) reported further experiments indicating inhibition of gene functions by histones. They found
that the very lysine rich fraction was the most inhibitive of RNA
synthesis. This fraction contained more proline than the other
fractions. The physical characteristics of the fractions appeared to
differ also; the temperature to denature DNA into single strands
was greatest for the most inhibitive, and all nucleohistones fractions required greater temperatures than did DNA alone.

Likewise, Izawa, Allfrey and Mirsky (1963), working with
giant lampbrush chromosomes of amphibian oocytes, found that
the addition of thymus gland histones to isolated nuclei inhibited
RNA synthesis. These histones consisted of two parts: one rich in
arginine and the other in lysine. The arginine portion was an
effective inhibitor of RNA synthesis whereas the lysine portion
produced a weak inhibition or was ineffectual. This result was in
contrast to those of Bonner and Huang (1964) discussed above.
They also found that active chromosomal material contained less
histone complexed with DNA than did the repressed material of
interphase calf thymus lymphocytes (Frenster, Allfrey and Mirsky,
1963). They revealed further by electron microscope autoradiography that the DNA active in RNA synthesis was mainly in the
diffuse, extended form rather than in the condensed, compact
masses (Littau *et al.*, 1964). Allfrey and Mirsky (1964a) suggested
a possible mechanism whereby histones could switch on or off
RNA synthesis at different loci along the chromosome. They
found that when histones of the arginine-rich type were subjected
to limited acetylation (uptake of acetate), they lost much of their
original capacity to inhibit RNA synthesis. This minor modification of histone structure was reversible.

Later work by Allfrey and Mirsky (1964b) showed agreement with the Bonner and Huang findings that the very lysine

rich fraction was most inhibitive. They reported also that inactive DNA was readily removed from isolated nuclei by deoxyribonuclease (DNase) but that active DNA required greater amounts of DNase or more prolonged incubation to be eliminated.

Busch (1965) indicated that histones cause a cessation of cell division and embryonic development in frogs' eggs.

Billen and Hnilica (1964) reported with *in vitro* studies with *E. coli* DNA polymerase, calf thymus DNA, and calf thymus histones that at sufficiently high concentrations of histone, DNA synthesis was completely suppressed. More than 50 per cent inhibition was obtained when the weight of DNA to histone was 2:1. The inhibition was accompanied by formation of a fibrous nucleohistone precipitate and loss of ultraviolet absorbing material, which paralleled the decline in DNA synthesis. Increasing the concentration of DNA brought about an almost complete reversal of the inhibition.

Goodwin and Sizer (1965) reported results which suggested that specificity of histones for a regulatory role resided in concentration rather than in type of histone present. They found that enzymatic activity in cultures of embryonic chick brain tissue was stimulated by low concentrations of histones but was repressed at higher concentrations. This control was shown to operate by an alteration of protein synthesis, presumably by changes in messenger RNA synthesis.

An interesting regulatory event has been shown with a variety of mammalian species including the human female (Grumbach, Morishima and Taylor, 1963). One of the X sex chromosomes in the somatic cells undergoes a change of state which first becomes manifest during early development. This X chromosome becomes highly condensed and is characterized by relative genetic inactivity. The other X chromosome in the female and the single X in the male is genetically active and in non-condensed form. Grumbach *et al* suggested an induction model patterned on the Jacob-Monod approach to account for these events.

The above regulatory events are only several of the many possible ones; furthermore, different types of gene regulation may occur in different cells or in the same cell at different times. Likewise, one should keep in mind that these mechanisms are intra-cellular events; obviously extracellular regulation occurs, also. Such regulation may take a number of forms. Probably one of the more important ones is the contribution of the reticular forma-tion of the brain stem in affecting the tonicity of other neural structures and possibly the upper portion in the thalamus serving as an integrating center (Penfield, 1960). (See Chapter 2.) An understanding of the overall regulatory functioning is the most basic problem for biology today but little is actually known con-cerning this function. Possibly with the tremendous advances at the molecular level, new insights may be suggested at higher levels and rapid development ensue on this important problem.

CHAPTER 7

DISORDERS OF DEFINITE
GENETIC ORIGIN

GENETIC LESIONS

Mental disorders consist essentially of two kinds, intellectual retardation and psychological anomalies. The first involves reduced mental keenness; the second consists of difficulties in adjusting emotionally and socially to one's environment (e.g., the psychoneuroses and psychoses). However, in many cases the two appear together, e.g., in many disorders of obviously genetic origin and in others of unknown etiology as well.

To illustrate the contribution of the genetic code to mental disorders, sickle cell anemia will provide a convenient prototype disorder. The value of sickle cell anemia is that it shows how a change of an amino acid at one site in a protein can result in severe effects. This condition provides clear evidence that genes control the amino acid sequence of a protein. In sickle cell anemia the erythrocytes form a sickle-shaped structure in contrast to normals whose erythrocytes do not sickle. The genetics of the sickle cell condition is relatively simple, resulting from a single recessive Mendelian gene (Hsia, 1959; Strauss 1960). The erythrocytes of heterozygotes (one allele normal, other allele for the sickling condition) will not normally sickle (only about one per cent of the red blood cells are sickled) but will sickle if the oxygen tension is artificially lowered. This individual has a sickle cell trait but shows no anemia. In the homozygous condition (both sickle cell alleles) 30 to 60 per cent of the erythrocytes in the venous circulation are sickled resulting in anemia.

The sickle cell erythrocytes contain a hemoglobin in which a valine is substituted for glutamic acid at one site in the polypeptide chain, indicating that gene change can result in a change of amino acid sequence in a protein. Thus the difference between a normal individual and one with sickle cell anemia resides in a chemical difference at a single site. A number of other abnormal hemoglobins have been reported which depend on an amino acid change at the same site (Hsia, 1959; Strauss, 1960). The implication of these results is that the DNA sites for the normal condition should differ from that of the anemic condition in a single trinucleotide portion (assuming a triplet codon) and should synthesize a different messenger RNA.

Having seen how a gene change can alter the amino acid sequence of a protein, let us now consider similar conditions which are directly related to intellectual and psychological disorders.

Disorders of genetic origin leading to psychological disorder are mainly of two kinds (Penrose, 1955). The first type involves recessive alleles and requires that both alleles be of the defective nature for the disorder to be expressed (homozygous). The individual lacks an enzyme because the defective alleles fail to make it. The heterozygote does not show the disorder because the single normal allele contains the necessary information for the manufacturing of the enzyme.

The second type is due to a dominant allele but may not appear in all cases. Sometimes the genetic error only gives rise to symptoms under special conditions or stresses.

The two types are concerned primarily with single sites in a chromosome, although genes at other sites may have some effect in that gene interaction is a common phenomenon (David and Snyder, 1962), i.e., the products of different genes may interact to affect overall behavior. The process in which regulator and operator genes regulate the production of RNA by structural genes is an example of gene interaction.

A third type should be added which results from more gross genetic errors such as chromosomal aberrations in which a whole chromosome, or portions of it, are added or deleted.

Only a few examples of genetic disorders will be discussed here.

Conditions Involving Recessive Alleles

Phenylketonuria or phenylpyruvic oligophrenia is a good example of a condition with intellectual and psychological symptoms which occurs through a genetic block of enzymatic action, due to recessive alleles at a single site in the chromosome. The symptoms usually include a retardation in intelligence, a possibility of epileptic symptoms and, occasionally, psychotic episodes. The disease is identified by an accumulation and excretion in the urine of phenylalanine and its pyruvic, lactic, acetic and other derivatives. Within a few weeks after birth, phenylpyruvic acid has inflicted permanent damage in brain tissue. Fortunately, the defect can be promptly detected and if the children are placed on special diets low in phenylalanine shortly after birth, they can escape all or nearly all the brain damage. Such a diet has less value in older infants and it appears to have no effect after six years of age (Hsia, 1959).

This disorder is due to a genetic block in the transformation of phenylalanine to tyrosine. A protein fraction required in enzymatic action for this transformation is deficient. Thus a block in a single step in a series of metabolic events leads to disastrous effects.

The genetics of phenylketonuria is relatively simple; it is inherited as though it were controlled by a single recessive Mendelian gene. In this case an enzyme in the liver is absent which suggests that a sequence of a number of trinucleotides in DNA and a single messenger RNA probably would be involved. The heterozygote is a carrier of phenylketonuria but does not show the extreme symptoms of the homozygote; however, a phenylalanine tolerance test shows that he metabolizes phenylalanine less well than normals (Hsia, 1959; Strauss, 1960).

It is not only possible to reverse the effects of this disorder, but a phenylketonuria-like state has been induced in monkeys and rats by a diet rich in phenylalanine (Waisman and Harlow, 1965). Such an event is an important and exciting contribution; it offers a model system that can be utilized to determine adverse brain damage changes and to evaluate the efficacy of possible chemical therapies.

There are other illustrations of metabolic disorders resulting from deficiencies of the genetic code at a single chromosomal site, e.g., congential amaurotic idiocy (defect of lipid metabolism) and galactosemia (defect of carbohydrate metabolism). In each of these the genetic information in the DNA sequence is such that some metabolic events differ from those of the usual condition and severe effects result.

Conditions Involving Dominant Alleles

These conditions are less easy to pinpoint than are the ones discussed above. These disorders are usually not manifested at birth but develop slowly, sometimes not occurring until late in life.

A striking example of this condition is Huntington's chorea. The cerebral cortex and basal ganglia begin to degenerate usually between the ages of thirty to fifty years. The degeneration is progressive and marked personality changes usually accompany the physical deterioration. The physical symptoms include: choreic movements becoming increasingly widespread and violent as the disease progresses; a jerking, irregular gait; facial grimaces; and slow, indistinct speech. The accompanying psychological symptoms typically include impairment of memory, irritability, impaired judgment and depression. The disease ends in dementia and eventually in death (Coleman, 1956).

Huntington's chorea is presumed to occur because of a heterozygous dominant gene (Penrose, 1955). Somewhat similar genetic disorders involving degeneration of the nervous system are Pick's disease, Alzheimer's disease and Parkinson's disorder.

Possibly the psychoses, schizophrenia and manic depressive disorders, are of this nature. Kallmann (1952) has presented evidence which strongly suggests a genetic predisposition in these disorders. Numerous biochemical irregularities have been reported in these psychotic conditions but no consistent metabolic peculiarities are present for all individuals. Many researchers (e.g., Rinkel and Denber, 1958; Rubin, 1959, 1962, Woolley, 1962) are attempting to locate the biochemical defects which are involved in these conditions.

Even though a dominant gene appears to be mainly responsible for these disorders, other genes must regulate the expression of the genetic predisposition in that in some cases the condition may not develop if the appropriate stressful events are not present. Thus large sequential sections of more than one DNA molecule would probably be involved with their corresponding messenger RNA's.

Conditions Involving Chromosomal Aberrations

An example of a more gross genetic condition leading to pathology is that of mongolism. This condition is usually characterized by intellectual retardation. Other defects of physical and psychological nature are usually present.

For many years there was a controversy as to whether this condition was genetic in nature. In recent years it has been conclusively indicated that genetic abnormalities lead to mongolism. The mongoloid has 47 chromosomes instead of 46 which the normal individual has; in a few cases only 46 chromosomes are present but one chromosome will be extra long because it contains a part of another chromosome. The abnormal condition is passed to offspring via "abnormal" ova. Presumably during the process of meiosis in the female when mature ova are formed, some gametes receive 24 chromosomes, others 22, rather than 23. This probably occurs when the single units are paired prior to separating to go to different gametes. However, in some cases the abnormality can occur after conception, i.e., during cell division.

The age of the mother appears to be a predisposing factor for older females show a greater number of mongoloids than younger mothers. The frequency of mongoloid births has been related also to external factors such as an epidemic of rubella. It has been suggested that viruses involved in rubella and other disorders may be responsible for this chromosomal aberrant condition (Robinson and Puck, 1965).

There has been a recent suggestion that one important metabolic deficiency of the mongoloid is opposite that of phenylketonuria. Because of the extra chromosome there is an excessive production of an enzyme which breaks down tryptophan, an essential amino acid for some brain proteins. Thus a greater amount of DNA and a duplication of genetic information would be present with the extra chromosome. Presumably extra messenger RNA's to synthesize the excessive enzyme are available because of the extra chromosomal material.

IMPLICATIONS FOR OTHER PSYCHOLOGICAL DISORDERS AND BEHAVIOR IN GENERAL

Although there are more than eighty conditions which can be traced to genetic lesions, there are only a few psychological disorders for which the genetic code can be definitely implicated. However, it is obvious that the genetic information contained within DNA molecules influences the development of psychopathologic symptoms. The exact mechanisms for this influence are obscure.

Likewise, it should be obvious that genetic information contained in the linear sequence of bases in DNA affects normal behavior. Again the exact mechanisms are obscure. This information probably specifies the quality and quantity of particular chemicals, including enzymes, which are synthesized and which regulate the behavior of the organism. The best example of the effects of varying chemicals on behavior is illustrated by variations in hormones of the endocrine system. The effects of hypothyroidism, hyperthyroidism and other extremes of endocrine activtiy are so prominent as to be included in any elementary text in psychology or other biological disciplines. However, it is not always realized that less extreme variations in hormones also influence behavior. Williams (1956) has investigated the variations in quantities of chemicals present in the saliva and in urine and has extended the concept of biochemical individuality which Garrod introduced in 1911. He expresses a biochemical profile for an individual in the form of a wheel with spokes radiating from the center. The length of each spoke corresponds to the quantity of a chemical for each individual; the shorter the line, the less is the quantity of a particular chemical. One can then attempt to relate the biochemical profile of an individual to his behavior. These biochemical patterns differ widely from one individual to the next but those of identical twins tend to resemble one another, thus expressing a genetic contribution to biochemical events. These variations in biochemistry are probably due to many genes.

With animals, gene differences have been related to temperamental and other behavioral capabilities, e.g., maze running ability, exploratory activity, general activity level and motivation, aggressiveness, susceptibility to audiogenic seizures, trainability, emotional responses, social behavior, etc. (David and Snyder, 1962; Broadhurst, 1960). Presumably the same results should occur with humans.

SECTION III

BEHAVIOR: ENVIRONMENTAL STIMULATION — MACROMOLECULAR EVENTS

CHAPTER 8

RESEARCH ON SIMPLE BEHAVIOR

T HE CHIEF EMPHASIS of researchers in molecular psychobiology has been on memory storage which is involved in learning events. Adequate handling of the memory process would then allow one to consider reactivation, forgetting and integration. However, a number of experiments have concentrated on less complex behavior, which will be considered first.

AMOUNTS OF NUCLEIC ACIDS IN BRAIN TISSUE

Some attention has been devoted to the gross DNA content of neural tissue. One study on rats, by Mandel, Harth and Borkowski, 1961), has indicated that the highest DNA content was in the grey and white matter of the cerebellum and in the olfactory bulb (Table 8-I). The lowest amounts were found in the spinal bulb, the mesencephalon and the thalamus. Moderate amounts were in the white and grey matter of the cerebrum, the hypothalamus, the hippocampus and the corpus striatum. The amount of DNA indicates the richness of the different areas in nuclei.

Vladimirov *et al.* (1961) reported that the amount of DNA was the same in the motor, visual, and auditory areas in layer 2 of cat cortex. Under hypoxic conditions a significant decrease occurred in the motor and visual area but not in the auditory area.

The RNA content of brain tissue has been studied also by Mandel *et al.* (op. cit.). They reported that the highest RNA content was in the olfactory bulb, the grey matter of the brain cortex and the cerebellum, the hypothalamus and the hippocampus (Table 8-I). Lower amounts were found in the corpus striatum, the thalamus and the white matter of the cerebrum and the cerebellum. The lowest figures occurred in the mesencephalon and the spinal bulb. The greatest RNA turnover was found in

107

the olfactory bulb, the hypothalamus and the grey matter of the brain cortex and the hippocampus.

The RNA/DNA ratio was highest in the grey matter of the cerebral cortex, the hippocampus, the thalamus, the corpus striatum and the hypothalamus (Table 8-I). The smallest ratio occurs in the olfactory bulb and the cerebellum. The greatest activity in RNA (indicated by P^{32} uptake) occurred in the olfactory bulb, hypothalamus, grey matter of the cortex and the cerebellum and the hippocampus.

TABLE 8-I
NUCLEIC ACIDS IN NERVE TISSUE OF RATS*

Brain Portion	In micrograms per gram of tissue (dry weight)		
	RNA	DNA	RNA/DNA
Olfactory bulb	70	100	.70
Cerebrum grey matter	65	36	1.72
Cerebellum grey matter	63	192	.30
Hippocampus	60	38	1.64
Hypothalamus	59	45	1.25
Corpus striatum	50	35	1.40
Thalamus	48	32	1.50
Cerebrum white matter	45	40	1.10
Cerebellum white matter	42	110	.40
Spinal bulb	38	33	1.18
Mesencephalon	37	32	1.20

*All values have been extrapolated from a figure by P. Mandel *et al.* (1961) and are approximate.

Vladimirov *et al.* (1961) reported that cytoplasmic RNA content in layer 2 of cat cortex was greatest in the motor area and least in the auditory area. Visual area RNA content was intermediate. The amount in the motor area was approximately three times as great as that in the auditory area. Under hypoxic conditions marked decreases in cytoplasmic RNA occurred in the motor and visual areas. RNA turnover was greater in the motor area than in the other areas.

Baranov and Pevzner (1963) found that the concentration of RNA in the inner layers of the motor and visual cortex of the rat brain was greater than that of the outer layers. The administration of hexenol four hours before decapitation caused an increase of RNA in all layers of the motor cortex except layer

6. Administration of caffein and camphor provided increases only in layer 5-6. The three drugs produced RNA increases in all layers of the visual cortex. The concentration of DNA in the motor cortex was lowest in the inner and outer layers and the three drugs produced the greatest change in these portions. Hexenol produced an increase in all layers in the visual cortex; camphor produced a decrement in all layers except the innermost one; caffein showed increases in the outer and inner layers. The concentration of cytoplasmic RNA in the cortical neurons of cat brain was higher in the inner layers for both motor and visual areas. When hypoxia was produced by clamping several arteries for six periods of five minutes in one hour, a considerable decresae in cytoplasmic RNA occurred (up to 70 per cent); the decrease was most marked in the inner and outer layers. The determinations were made with microchemical and microspectrophotometric procedures. In the various experiments cited, it appeared that the nucleic acids in the inner and outer layers were more labile than was the middle layers.

RESEARCH CONCERNING DEVELOPMENT, MOTOR ACTIVITY AND STIMULATION

Development and Long Term Aspects

During development one would expect that each brain DNA site concerned with potential for particular functions would increase the amounts of RNA which it synthesizes so that protein synthesis and other related events could occur. In general, this is what has been reported. The reports do not always show that the amounts of RNA increase with age in development; however, the RNA/DNA ratio is a more suitable index of relative RNA synthesis than is the amount of RNA per unit weight of tissue. This ratio tends to increase during important developmental stages. For example, Leslie (1955) summarized the nucleic acid content of tissues and cells with a table which showed that in brain tissue, the RNA/DNA ratio increased from prenatal to postnatal life even though the amount of RNA did not always show the same consistent trend nor did DNA vary consistently (Table 8-II). Furthermore, the consistent increase in ratio over

Molecular Psychobiology

these some ages did not usually occur for other tissues, *viz.*, liver, heart and muscle.

A study has been conducted in the author's laboratory to determine neurochemical changes during development for normal and visually deprived white rats. Normal animals (controls-C)

TABLE 8-II
AMOUNTS OF RNA AND DNA, AND RNA/DNA RATIOS
FOR TISSUES OVER AGE
(Leslie, 1955)

| | Micrograms per 100 mg fresh tissue | | |
	RNA	DNA	RNA/DNA Ratio
Brain (chick embryo)			
8 days	50	29	1.72
13 days	40	12	3.20
Hatching	45	12	3.75
2-day chick	53	10	5.30
Brain (chick embryo)			
10 days	29	15	1.91
13 days	32	12	2.80
16 days	39	12	3.26
19 days	41	11	3.86
Liver (chick embryo)			
8 days	118	27	4.40
15 days	86	24	3.58
Hatching	90	19	4.74
2-day chick	89	19	4.68
Heart (chick embryo)			
8 days	50	17	2.94
14.5 days	47	18	2.61
Hatching	49	20	2.45
2-day chick	38	19	2.00
Muscle (chick embryo)			
11.5 days	45	21	2.16
17.5 days	47	20	2.35
Hatching	36	12	3.00
2-day chick	38	14	2.72
Muscle (chick embryo)			
9 days	39	19	2.03
16 days	30	20	1.50
18 days	34	23	1.48
20 days	24	12	2.00
Liver (rat)			
10 days	58	33	1.76
21 days	52	24	2.29
Male: 41 days	85	21	4.21
80 days	82	18	4.59
182 days	78	17	4.62
Liver (pullet)			
1 day	56	21	2.70
32 days	57	31	1.82
123 days	76	32	2.36
180 days	84	31	2.70
Cerebral cortex (guinea pig)			
25th day of gestation			1.00
Adult			3.30

were sacrificed at zero, fifteen, thirty, fifty, seventy-five, one hundred, 115, 135, 160 and 185 days of age; the amounts of DNA, RNA and proteins, and the RNA/DNA, protein/DNA and protein/RNA, ratios for eleven neural and one nonneural tissues, were determined. These tissues are: anterior, medial and posterior portions of the dorsal cortex (the latter sectioned into the visual and auditory areas), the same portions of the ventral cortex; cerebral hemispheres less the cortex, cerebellum, upper brain stem, lower brain stem and kidney. Another group of animals, littermates of the first group, have the eyes removed at fifteen days of age (prior to the opening of the eyelids) and are sacrificed at thirty, fifty, seventy-five and one hundred days of age (Experimentals-E). A third littermate group (E's) have the eyes removed at one hundred days and are sacrificed at 115, 135, 160 and 185 days. The same measures were determined for these animals to ascertain the effects of visual deprivation.

A number of molecular biology studies (Beerman and Clever, 1964; Edstrom, 1964; Izawa, Allfrey and Mirsky, 1963; Karlson, 1962; Schneiderman and Gilbert, 1964) suggest that the RNA/DNA ratio can be used as an index of functional activity. In these studies the RNA/DNA ratio at active DNA sites was much greater than at inactive DNA sites. Furthermore, in that the amounts of protein in a cell are much greater than are the amounts of RNA, this latter ratio would appear to be a more sensitive indicator than the former, except possibly in nuclear material. Relative protein synthesis, i.e., the amount of protein per RNA (protein/RNA ratio) is another possible index. These three ratios were employed in this study because functional activity of cells during development was of concern.

In this experiment data have been obtained through the one-hundred-day point. The results show a number of interesting points (Tables 8-III to 8-VIII).

The amounts of RNA/g of tissue remain approximately the same from fifteen to one hundred days in all cortical tissues, with slight variation (about 0.3 to 0.6 mg/g). (The cortex was not separated from the cerebral hemispheres at birth.) In the cerebellum there is a sharp drop from about 1.5 mg at birth to about 0.5 mg at thirty days and thereafter. The cerebral hemispheres, upper and lower brain stem and kidney show essentially the same trend as the cerebellum except that at birth the kidney contains about 5 mg/g of tissue; the values for the other tissues are between 1 and 2 mg/g of tissue.

The values for DNA appear to be similar in all cortical portions and in the upper and lower brain stem, a V-shaped curve with the lowest amounts occurring at fifty days of age (between

TABLE 8-III

MEAN AMOUNT OF RNA (IN MICROGRAMS) PER GRAM OF TISSUE FOR NEURAL AND NONNEURAL TISSUES FROM 0 TO 100 DAYS

Tissues	Days					
	0	15	30	50	75	100
1E*		444	298	342	549	402
1C			295	410	462	407
2		496	392	331	433	390
3		463	239	431	542	443
4		556	332	395	432	390
5		581	394	446	457	422
6		492	334	335	543	495
7		420	290	404	631	584
8E			462	426	486	422
8C	1551	793	451	438	462	443
9	1298	545	379	378	442	397
10	1744	487	381	376	401	376
11	1744	584	390	340	377	340
12	4889	726	755	843	1013	850

*In this and later tables (to Table 8-VIII) : 1 = anterior ventral cortex; 2 = medial ventral cortex; 3 = posterior ventral cortex; 4 = anterior dorsal cortex (motor area) ; 5 = medial dorsal cortex (somesthetic area) ; 6 = posterior dorsal cortex (visual area); 7 = posterior dorsal cortex (auditory area); 8 = cerebellum; 9 = cerebral hemispheres; 10 = upper brain stem; 11 = lower brain stem; 12 = kidney; E = enucleated animals; C = seeing animals.

TABLE 8-IV

MEAN AMOUNT OF DNA (IN MICROGRAMS) PER GRAM OF TISSUE

Tissues	Days					
	0	15	30	50	75	100
1E		827	458	225	661	349
1C			429	246	579	491
2		524	623	245	409	274
3		675	663	143	586	309
4		565	369	213	326	274
5		622	372	300	364	345
6		704	593	222	578	504
7		1103	452	156	564	456
8E	699	3056	2280	1430	1743	2278
8C		3056	1965	1108	1834	2346
9	1578	419	272	180	371	448
10	473	398	341	215	358	455
11	473	676	417	194	344	386
12	1853	2814	1657	1016	1008	1176

TABLE 8-V
MEAN AMOUNT OF PROTEIN (IN MILLIGRAMS)
PER GRAM OF TISSUE

Tissues	Days					
	0	15	30	50	75	100
1E		8.2	14.0	34.9	38.1	9.6
1C			11.5	34.1	27.0	9.4
2		11.5	17.3	30.9	27.9	9.7
3		7.7	11.1	27.0	22.7	12.8
4		9.7	16.1	37.3	39.3	15.0
5		11.4	20.3	41.3	36.3	17.1
6		10.2	12.4	25.7	37.8	11.8
7		6.6	13.5	39.5	52.5	15.1
8E	9.1	13.1	22.8	40.1	25.8	15.9
8C			23.5	35.7	30.5	17.8
9	23.1	13.5	22.2	36.5	30.2	17.9
10	13.2	12.5	21.8	35.3	30.2	17.8
11	13.2	12.7	20.7	29.4	25.6	13.5
12	21.4	13.7	25.9	45.0	43.1	27.3

TABLE 8-VI
MEAN RNA/DNA RATIOS

Tissues	Days					
	0	15	30	50	75	100
1E		0.56	0.66	1.61	0.72	1.17
1C			0.74	1.99	0.81	0.94
2		1.02	0.75	1.69	1.16	1.47
3		0.82	0.36	3.11	0.99	1.60
4		1.08	1.08	2.34	1.47	1.47
5		1.09	1.19	1.62	1.27	1.31
6		0.83	0.58	2.64	1.00	1.30
7		0.39	0.60	2.60	1.18	1.49
8E	2.37	0.28	0.23	0.30	0.28	0.19
8C			0.28	0.41	0.27	0.19
9	0.83	1.46	1.52	2.13	1.23	0.92
10	4.86	1.41	1.15	1.77	1.12	0.87
11	4.86	1.37	0.98	1.85	1.10	0.94
12	3.39	0.30	0.49	0.92	1.01	0.73

TABLE 8-VII
MEAN PROTEIN/DNA RATIOS

Tissues	Days					
	0	15	30	50	75	100
1E		11	52	171	57	29
1C			39	163	48	23
2		25	41	154	78	35
3		15	25	189	46	44
4		17	65	219	133	63
5		19	73	146	106	54
6		15	28	196	65	34
7		5	51	257	93	34
8E	13	5	11	28	15	7
8C			14	32	17	8
9	15	39	86	202	84	41
10	28	37	64	167	84	41
11	28	34	56	164	75	37
12	16	5	16	45	43	24

0.1 and 0.3 mg). In the cerebellum the value is lowest at birth (0.7 mg), increases sharply at fifteen days (about 3 mg), decreases to lowest value at fifty days (slightly more than 1 mg), and increases slowly thereafter. Related to the drastic increase from zero to fifteen days is the observation that the cerebellum at birth and at various periods up to fifteen days did not cover the lower portion of the mesencephalon as it does at later ages. The size of the cerebellum is approximately the same as the mesencephalon at birth but grows rapidly during the early days of life. This latter result, along with the realization that the amount of DNA in a given amount of tissue is used as an indication of the number of cells (Zamenhof *et al.*, 1964), suggest that a rapid increase in number of cells occurs in the cerebellum after birth, possibly in both neural and neuroglial cells.

TABLE 8-VIII
MEAN PROTEIN/RNA RATIOS

Tissues	Days					
	0	15	30	50	75	100
1E		19	86	103	87	24
1C			52	84	61	23
2		23	61	94	65	25
3		16	72	70	42	29
4		18	59	96	91	38
5		20	62	95	79	41
6C		20	57	80	79	25
6E			50	75	56	24
7		17	112	97	82	25
8E	6	17	56	94	53	38
8C			60	83	66	40
9	18	28	63	97	69	45
10	8	27	63	96	76	48
11	8	22	61	88	68	40
12	6	22	40	54	45	32

The cerebral hemispheres show approximately 1.5 mg of DNA at birth. There is a sharp drop at fifteen days and the lowest value is reached at fifty days and a gradual increase thereafter. The DNA trend for the kidney is similar to that of the cerebellum; however, the value at birth is greater in the former (2 mg/g) and the amount remains the same from fifty to one hundred days (1 mg/g).

Most cortical portions show a peak in amounts of proteins/g of tissue at fifty days (between 20 and 40 mg) with the one-hundred-day values about equal to those of the fifteen- or thirty-day periods. In the anterior ventral cortex, visual cortex, and auditory cortex, the values at fifty and seventy-five days tend to be the highest ones. The cerebellum shows a slow increase in proteins from birth to fifty days and then a decline to the fifteen-day level at one hundred days. The upper and lower brain stems show the same pattern: same values at birth and fifteen days, slow increase to a peak at fifty days, and a decline to the fifteen-day level by one hundred days. The cerebral hemispheres decline from zero to fifteen days, gradually increase to fifty days, and decrease thereafter. The kidney pattern is similar to that of the cerebral hemispheres except that the fifty and seventy-five-day points show large values.

The decreases in amounts of RNA and DNA in some tissues are consistent with those reported by other investigators (e.g., Schade and Pascoe, 1964) and do not mean that the amounts per cell are decreasing. Presumably DNA is remaining constant and RNA increasing slightly. Because the amounts are per gram of tissue the amount per cell could be increasing but still show decreasing value per gram of tissue. These decreases probably indicate that cells are growing rapidly and that RNA and DNA constitute a lesser proportion of the total cell constituency with increasing protein being largely responsible for the decrements. The decreasing amounts of protein after fifty or seventy-five days probably reflects increasing amounts of constituents not evaluated in this study. A possible candidate would be phospholipids whose activity tends to increase with functional activity, as is the case with RNA and proteins as well (Palladin and Vladirmirov, 1956). Alternatively, water content per cell may be increasing.

In the two indices of functional activity, protein/DNA and RNA/DNA ratios, the patterns are generally the same. All brain tissues show a peak at fifty days and a sharp drop before and after this period. At one hundred days the values for the protein/DNA ratio tend to be similar to those at fifteen or thirty days. In the RNA/DNA ratio the one hundred day values for cortical tissue are generally higher than for the thirty day point and approach the peak values at fifty days. It is as if a second peak beyond one hundred days will appear. The cerebellum shows a drop from birth to fifteen days, a gradual increase to fifty days, and a decrement thereafter in both ratios. The cerebellum shows the lowest ratios of all brain tissue, being the richest in DNA. The brain stem portions show the same pattern as the cerebellum for the RNA/DNA ratio but in the protein/DNA ratio there is a gradual increase from birth to fifty days and then a decrement thereafter. The cerebral hemispheres show this latter trend for both ratios. The kidney shows the same trend with both ratios: a decrease from birth to fifteen days, increase to peaks at fifty and seventy-five days, and a slight decrement at one hundred days. The kidney is almost as rich in DNA as is the cerebellum.

In the mature rat (one hundred days), the RNA/DNA ratio varies about one for all brain tissue except the cerebellum which is about 0.2. The kidney is intermediate in value between the cerebellum and other brain tissue. This trend is the same in protein/DNA ratio also.

The RNA/DNA ratio at birth is lowest in the cerebral hemisipheres (0.83) and highest in the brain stem (4.86). Essentially the same result occurs in the protein/DNA ratio. This suggests greatest functional activity is in the brain stem, which is what one would expect.

The protein/RNA values for cortical tissue are similar to those obtained with the protein/DNA ratio: peak at fifty days with the 100 day value about the same as the fifteen-day value. All other brain portions and kidney show a gradual increase from birth to fifty days and a slow decrease thereafter.

The results of the three ratios (plus the DNA and protein data) suggest strongly that the fifty-day point is one of great cellular activity in the rat. This age is one of "puberty" with maturity occurring at between seventy-five and one hundred days. Probably this is a period of great growth for neural and non-neural tissues. Related to this result is the report by Brizzee, Vogt and Kharetchka (1964) that the fifty-day point is the one of least cell density in the cerebral cortex of the white rat. At ten days there are approximately 100,000 cells/mm^3; at fifty days, 70,000; and by one hundred days the value had risen to 90,000.

The protein/RNA ratio data indicate that a given amount of RNA produces more protein at fifty days than at any other period. This suggests the presence of more long-lived RNA's at this period. Such RNA's have been reported in other mammalian tissues (Dure and Waters, 1965; Scott and Bell, 1965).

This conclusion would imply that RNA degradation processes are reduced in activity or else that specific RNA's are produced around the fifty-day period which are more resistant to degradation events. Another possibility is that ribosomal activity increases at this age. Obviously both events may be involved.

It is interesting to note that the pattern of macromolecular change in the kidney during development is grossly similar to that in brain tissue. However, there are several important differences. The kidney shows peaks of cellular activity at both fifty and seventy-five days; it is richer in RNA, DNA and protein/g than most brain tissues; it has lower RNA/DNA and protein/DNA ratios than all brain tissues except the cerebellum, and it is lowest in protein/RNA ratio.

The enucleated and seeing animals differed significantly only in the anterior ventral cortex and in the cerebellum. The anterior ventral cortex is part of the olfactory system in the rat; the E animals showed greater mean protein/DNA and protein/RNA ratios than C animals. This difference suggests sensory compensation, i.e., the E animals when deprived of a prominent sense (vision) utilize another prominent sense (olfaction) more so than do animals with both senses intact. The results with other sensory systems (audition and somesthesis) did not suggest sensory compensation.

In the cerebellum the seeing animals had greater mean RNA/DNA and protein/DNA ratios than the enucleated animals. This difference is probably related to the fact that the cerebellum receives visual input but the exact pathways are unknown (Brookhart, 1960); however, the cerebellum is involved in coordinating equilibration and motor activities and the differences may be relevant to these functions.

In the visual cortex there had been the expectation that the mean values in the RNA/DNA and protein/DNA ratios would be greater for C than for E. There were no significant differences. However, the E group did have a greater mean value for the protein/RNA ratio. No comparisons for protein, RNA or DNA showed significant differences in this tissue. Thus the exact significance of the differences in the protein/RNA ratio is not clear.

The lack of prominent differences between C and E in the visual cortex may merely indicate that differences are present but that the prcoedures were not sensitive enough to detect these differences. However, it is possible that in seeing animals the visual cortex serves visual purposes but in animals whose eyes were removed this cortex may function for other specific events.

An evaluation of this latter possibility will be provided by the analysis of the data from the rats enucleated at one hundred days. If the visual cortex functions mainly for visual purposes in the seeing animal, there should be a decrement in functional activity indices if the eyes are removed at maturity.

Talwar, Chopra, and Goel (1964) demonstrated that the RNA/DNA and protein/DNA ratios in the cerebral cortex of adult rabbits was 110 and 337 per cent higher, respectively, than in the cortex of newborn animals. Several other areas of the brain showed lower increases.

Holger Hyden has developed precise dissection and analytic procedures which allowed him to determine the amount of RNA per cell. He dissected motor nerve cells from humans killed in accidents and found that the amount of RNA increases significantly from the third year of life to age forty, remains fairly constant to about sixty, and then declines rapidly (1961).

Related to the Hyden result is a report by Kral and Sved (1963) concerning RNase activity in the blood. They included individuals from about twenty to one-hundred years of age. There was a consistent increase with age; the enzymatic activity at age sixty was about 25 per cent greater than at age twenty and at one-hundred years, about 50 per cent greater.

If the increase in RNase activity in blood is representative of enzymatic activity in the brain, and if the spinal cord RNA changes are representative of brain RNA events, then one could say that amounts of RNA decrease in old age because of RNase activity. Related to this possibility is the indication that in mice, irradiation of spleen cells resulted in a drastic decrease in DNA content which was paralleled by a large increase in DNase (Kurnick and Nokay, 1963). For example, mice irradiated by 800 roentgens had 21 per cent as much DNA in spleen cells as non-irradiated mice but had five times as much DNase. On the other hand, the rate of RNA synthesis by DNA sites probably also decreases during later life; this event could account for the lesser RNA available.

Kjelgaard and Kurland (1963) showed that the ratio of ribosomal RNA to DNA increases proportionately with growth rate in bacteria but the same ratio with transfer RNA was constant irrespective of growth. In the absence of protein synthesis, transfer RNA synthesis was constant but ribosomal RNA synthesis decreased. These results suggest that ribosomal RNA amounts are related to protein synthesis and to growth, as one would expect from other data. It has been indicated in other bacterial studies that the ratio of RNA to protein varies with the stage of growth and the growth rate and the amount of ribosomes also varies with the growth phase (Grunberg-Manago, 1963). Roberts, McQuillen and Roberts (1959) summarized studies on growth kinetics of *Salmonella typhinurium* cultures which showed that during growth a greater number of ribosomes were present. Calculations suggested that the rate of protein synthesis was a direct function of ribosomal content at all growth rates.

Presumably the above increases in RNA/DNA ratios during development are reflecting mainly the ribosomal effect because of the bacterial data and because this RNA constitutes 80 per cent or mroe of cellular RNA and is extremely stable.

An abrupt increase in the number of Nissl bodies (ribosomes) in the cerebral cortex about half way through gestation in the fetal pig was reported by Flexner (1952). Before the forty-first day Nissl substance was absent; at about the forty-first day it appeared and rapidly accumulated over a four-day period. Attending this rapid increase was an increase in the size of cells and a rise in activity of a number of enzymes.

The effect of chemicals on the growth of fungi was reported

by Wagener and Romano (1963). It has been known for a long time that zinc has a profound effect on the growth and physiological behavior of many fungi. Wegener and Romano added zinc sulfate to a growing culture of *Rhizopus nigricans*. RNA synthesis increased immediately; protein synthesis was also stimulated. The increase in RNA during the first three and one-half hours was 2.7 times as great in the presence of zinc sulfate as it was in its absence. During this same period the increase in protein was only 1.6 times as great in the presence of zinc as in its absence. In the following five and one-half hours, both RNA and protein increased at the same relative rate. After fifteen and one-half hours both RNA and proteins were approximately three times as great for zinc cultures as for those without zinc. The authors postulated that the zinc sulfate stimulated growth through a primary effect on RNA synthesis. It was not possible to determine whether the zinc stimulated synthesis of all RNA's or whether there was a selective effect on ribosomal, messenger, or transfer RNA.

Research by Neidle and Waelsch (1964) suggested that histones change during development. Using disc electrophoresis in polyacrylamide gels, they found that the pattern for histones in the liver and brain of the young rat was different than that in the adult rat. The histone patterns of the thymus of the young and adult rats were the same and corresponded to those of the young brain and liver. The differences between young and adult animals were in both intensity and spacing of the bands which separated during electrophoresis. They were unable to indicate clearly whether the differences were of qualitative or quantitative nature; furthermore, they allowed for the possibility that the differences were due to differences in extractability of the histones from young and adult organs.

Suzuki, Korey and Terry (1964) investigated *in vitro* protein synthesis of brain microsomal systems in grey and white matter of young and adult rats and humans. They found that both the grey and white matter of twelve-day-old rats were as active as adult grey matter in lysine incorporation whereas adult white matter was approximately 50 per cent as active. To account for the high rate of activity in twelve-day-old white matter, they suggested that active myelination processes were prominent. In a small number of humans (five) they found that lysine-incorporating activity of the younger individuals (thirty-forty year range) was greater than in older individuals (over fifty).

Altman (1966) has used autoradiography to determine the effects of experience on DNA activity in glial cells. One group of rats was reared for one hundred days in an enriched environment. He found greater labeling of DNA by tritiated thymidine in glial cells of the neocortex for the former than for the latter. The differences varied from 32 to 118 per cent with the greatest differences occurring in the white matter of the cortex. These results suggested that glial cells increased in number during the stimulation events of the one hundred days.

Stimulation and Activity — Short Term Effects

The effects of stimulation and activity on the gross amounts of DNA are minimal or nonexistent. The average DNA content appears to be relatively stable even during marked physiological alterations of cells whose nuclear size and protein content may vary widely (Alfert, 1957). Leslie (1955) summarized numerous studies and reported that changes in DNA content were related to changes in cell number and not to stimulation conditions. There is general agreement concerning the absence of DNA turnover in rapidly growing cells and a limited rate of turnover in slowly growing cells or in resting bacteria (Sinsheimer, 1960).

Although DNA, in general, shows great stability, the picture with RNA is different. RNA varies from cell to cell and is very active metabolically (Ris, 1957). LeBaron (1959) indicated that cytochemical research provides evidence for increased activity of cellular RNA and proteins. He concluded that there was ample evidence for the active turnover of various lipid, protein and nucleic acid structural constituents during stimulation.

Leslie (1955) discussed regenerating tissue, dietary aspects, neoplastic tissues, hormonal influences and various pathological conditions and stressed the increased activity of RNA and proteins in these cases.

Investigations of chromosomes of insects have shown puffing at specific chromosomal sites which are assumed to be sites of active DNA in which RNA synthesis is proceeding. These sites of activity appear to be at different loci in different tissue and at different loci in the same tissue at different times (Beerman and Clever, 1964). The degree of puffing at one site was directly related to the number of granules in salivary secretions. Karlson (1962) has reported that a hormone, ecdysone, is able to bring about puffing in the insect, *Chironomus,* and soon thereafter the organism goes from the larva to the pupa state.

Hyden (1961) reported that the RNA content of the nerve cell ranks with the highest of all cells in the body. He reported that if an animal is deprived of stimulation in one of the sensory systems, for example, in vision or hearing, the neurons in that system do not develop biochemically. The structure appeared normal but the nerve cell was impoverished in both RNA and proteins. Hyden maintained that individuals with certain psychic disorders have smaller amounts of RNA and proteins in ganglion cells of the central nervous system than do normal individuals. Administration of malononitrile to these individuals increased the content of these substances. Egyhazi and Hyden (1961) indicated that the malononitrile action was due to the formation of a dimer of malononitrile, tricyanoamino-propene. This chemical hastens RNA synthesis; it has an anti-thyroid effect but causes no observable toxic effect if given in suitable amounts. They reported that small amounts of this compound caused an increase of 25 per cent in the amounts of proteins and RNA in nerve cells and a decrease of 45 per cent in glial RNA. The cytosine in nerve cells decreased significantly and in glial cells the cytosine showed a 20 per cent decrease. The guanine in glial RNA decreased also by 25 per cent.

Jacob and Sirlin (1964) reported that this drug greatly stimulates the incorporation of uridine in RNA of insect salivary glands. The drug also is able to prevent actinomycin D from inhibiting RNA synthesis. Gerard (1963; Chamberlain, Halick and Gerard, 1963) indicated that malononitrile will increase the fixation of a postural asymmetry. A unilateral lesion in the cerebellum produces a postural asymmetry in the legs which is due to an asymmetrical relay of impulses coming down the two sides of the cord. By cutting the cord the asymmetry may be abolished. They found that if the cord was cut within forty-five minutes the asymmetry was usually eliminated; otherwise, the asymmetry persisted indefinitely. By speeding up RNA synthesis in neurons with malononitrile the fixation time for asymmetry was decreased to twenty-five to thirty minutes. Using 8-azaguanine to retard RNA synthesis, the fixation time was increased to seventy minutes.

Hyden and Lange (1960) investigated the relationship between glial and neural cells during various activities. They found that when rabbits were rotated on a circular disk (twenty-five minutes/day for seven days) to provide vestibular stimulation there was a significant increase in RNA and proteins, and in certain enzymatic activity (i.e., cytochrome oxidase and succinoxidase) in the giant Deiter cells in the vestibular nucleus of the medulla. In the oligodendroglia surrounding the nerve cells, there was a 30 per cent decrease in the amount of RNA and more than 300 per cent decrease in cytochrome oxdiase activity. The authors suggested that these results show that the nerve and glial cells are linked energetically into a functional system.

Hyden (1961) stated that when a sensory or motor system was stimulated, within limits, the individual nerve cells showed an increased content of RNA, proteins and lipids. This increase began when the level of stimulation increased and reversed within hours when it decreased. When an animal became exhausted, the RNA content fell below normal but the level was restored with rest. When a cell was damaged by a strong sound, radiation, virus attack or poison, the RNA decreased drastically.

Geiger, Yamasoki and Lyons (1956) stimulated the brain cortex of cats and found a change of RNA in the stimulated areas, which was reversible in minutes.

Likewise, Morrell (1961) has shown gross changes in RNA of nerve cells. He stimulated a portion of the cortex with ethyl chloride spray. The homologous tissue of the opposite hemisphere showed activity during this stimulation. At first the activity in the opposite hemisphere appeared only when the stimulated cortex was active. After a time, the tissue in the nonstimulated area showed spontaneuos excitation even when it was isolated from the stimulated hemisphere by cutting its connections. Biochemical analysis of the neurons in the isolated tissue showed a change in the RNA content.

Kogan (1964) investigated the effect of light flashes on RNA content. He reported that a rise in RNA content occurred when electrical potentials showed excitation of cells in the visual cortex. A redistribution of the RNA from one part of the dendrites to another was observed also in some cases. Those cells which did not respond to light flashes did not show a rise of RNA.

Talwar *et al.* (1966) found that the synthesis of RNA in the occipital cortex of monkeys exposed to dark for forty-five minutes or two hours was greater than for monkeys exposed to flickering light for the same period. RNA synthesis was determined by the amount of incorporation of radioactive precursors of RNA in the occipital cortex.

The effects of drastic stimulation has generally been to decrease RNA content. Noach, Bunk and Wijling (1962) used ECS with rats and sacrificed them either thirty seconds or seventy-five seconds later. Slices of parietal cortex were removed and DNA and RNA extracted. There was no difference between shocked and unshocked rats at thirty seconds but at seventy-five seconds the RNA content of the shocked animals was slightly less. There was no effect on the DNA content. They reported also a decrement in RNA content following administration of phenobarbital.

Mihailovic *et al.* (1958) sacrificed cats one minute after the last convulsion following ECS. The exact time of sacrifice following the onset fo ECS was not specified; presumably the time of sacrifice was approximately five minutes after introduction of ECS in that convulsions may last about this time. There was no effect on DNA but RNA decreases occurred in all central nervous system tissues analyzed (Table 8-IX). The decreases varied from approximately 10 to 30 per cent with the greatest decrements occurring in frontal, temporal and occipital cortices, hippocampus, cerebellar cortex, thalamus and hypothalamus.

Talwar, Sadasivudu and Chitre (1961) also showed a decrease in the RNA content of the brain of rats decapitated during Metrazol-induced convulsions. They reported a reduction of 10 per cent in total RNA amounts. The decrement was greatest in nuclear RNA with a loss of 25 per cent; cytoplasmic RNA decreased by 6 per cent. If the animal was sacrificed during the preconvulsive stage, however, the rate of RNA synthesis in brain tissue showed a slight increase. The values returned to normal in the post convulsive phase (Talwar *et al.*, 1966). Accompanying the increase during the preconvulsive stage were increases in the RNA/DNA and protein/DNA ratios (Chitre and Talwar, 1963); likewise, accompanying the RNA decrements during the convulsive stage were decreases in these ratios.

TABLE 8-IX
DIFFERENCES BETWEEN SHOCKED AND NONSHOCKED
CATS IN RNA CONTENT OF CERTAIN CENTRAL
NERVOUS SYSTEM REGIONS
(modified from Milhailovic *et al.*, 1958)

Region of CNS	Control	ECS*
Frontal cortex	299.0 (27.6) **	223.0 (14.1)
Occipital cortex	303.4 (28.7)	234.8 (15.7)
Temporal cortex	305.6 (11.0)	241.6 (3.2)
Hippocampus	290.3 (27.8)	218.0 (31.8)
Cerebellar cortex	337.6 (23.9)	258.6 (13.7)
Cerebral White matter	148.8 (11.4)	121.4 (22.3)
Caudate Nucleus	282.2 (19.1)	211.5 (26.1)
Thalamus	232.4 (22.7)	162.3 (14.6)
Hypothalamus	265.0 (23.1)	193.0 (34.7)
Midbrain	206.1 (15.1)	152.3 (32.7)
Pons	168.0 (19.3)	153.7 (15.4)
Medulla	170.1 (7.4)	136.5 (19.5)
Spinal cord	140.2 (11.1)	113.3 (16.5)

*Values in micrograms per 10 milligrams of dried tissue.
**Standard deviations in parentheses.

Metrazol-induced convulsions brought about a significant increase greater than 20 per cent in RNA content in the gastrocnemius muscle of the rat but had no effect on RNA content in the liver (Chitre, Chopra and Talwar, 1964).

Related to the loss of RNA during convulsions is the report by Takahashi and Aprison (1964) that a decrease of 43 to 45 per cent occurs in the ACh concentrations in the brain during this state. They stated that ACh levels vary inversely with the degree of functional activity of the brain, being highest during normal sleep or under anesthesia. Other individuals (Pepeu and Mantegazzini, 1964) have obtained similar results. However, amounts of ACh *released* from the cortex varies directly with functional activity (see Chapter 3).

Hyden (1964) reported an interesting experiment with barracuda fish involving drastic stimulation. These animals were exhausted experimentally by twenty to thirty minutes of motor activity (hard swimming) and then the motor cells in the spinal cord (the anterior horn) were dissected and RNA extracted. The amount of RNA (in micromicrograms per cell) was as follows: control, 3244; experimentals immediately after motor activity, 3416; one hour later, 3637; two hours later, 3658; three hours later, 3723; four hours later, 4029; five hours later, 4019. Thus a drastic increase in RNA occurred during and after the motor activity. This result is not consistent with other work by Hyden discussed above. Ordinarily RNA content increases during the early stages of activity but decreases when the animal is exhausted.

A number of investigators have utilized uptake of radioactive materials into nucleic acids to assess relative activity during various behavioral events. Palladin and Vladimirov (1956) reported the following.

1) In animals with a well developed cortex, e.g., dogs, the renewal rate of RNA and phosphoproteins is highest in the cerebral hemispheres. This was true for both the cortex and the white matter. The turnover rate of phospholipids was highest in the cortex.

2) In animals with a lesser developed cerebral cortex, e.g., rabbits, the turnover rate of RNA in the grey matter is lower than in the white matter or cerebellum. The renewal rate in the spinal cord is also low. The rate of phosphoprotein renewal of the cortex and cerebellum was lower than in brain stem areas.

3) The renewal of RNA and phospholipids in the motor area of dogs (parietal and frontal lobes) proceeded at a higher rate than in the auditory (temporal lobe) or optic (occipital lobe) areas.

4) The cerebral cortex and the cerebellum exhibited the highest rate of protein renewal; the spinal cord showed the lowest rate.

5) In rats subjected to stimulation of the brain there was a 20 per cent increased renewal rate in RNA and 150 per cent rate in phospholipids.

6) Presentation of a conditional stimulus resulted in an increase in the RNA metabolism in that area of the cortex in which

the stimulation was primarily localized, e.g., if an acoustic signal is the conditioned stimulus, the increase is in the auditory area.

7) Electrical stimulation showed an increase in protein metabolism of brain tissue as well.

8) During a twenty-four-hour sleep induced by urethane and medinal, the relative specific activity of RNA, phosphoproteins and phospholipids decreased 20 to 28 per cent. Amytal produced a more profound sleep and a greater decrement on brain components, including proteins.

9) Hibernating susliks (ground squirrels) showed a decrease in the metabolism of RNA and phospholipids.

The above results show that when the organism is functionally active, there is increased synthesis of RNA; when functionally inactivated, decreased synthesis occurs in RNA. In general, changes in phosphoproteins, phospholipids, lipoproteins and proteins are in the same direction as the RNA changes. Other reports (Costa, 1965) also indicate that protein turnover changes during excitation and inhibition.

In an excellent review in a recent volume, Pevzner (1966) discusses numerous other studies which are consistent with the above statement about RNA, i.e., this nucleic acid is directly related to the functional activity of the organism. Another interesting review is by Talwar *et al.* (1966).

Altman has used autoradiography to determine the activity of DNA and proteins. He found (1962) that tritiated (H^3) thymidine was incorporated in the DNA of glia cells of rat brain tissue following the production of brain lesions. Some autoradiographs showed labeling at neural sites not associated with the lesion. Treatment with DNase removed the label. Altman suggested that this result indicated that new neurons may come into existence in the brain of an adult rat. Koenig (1958) obtained C^{14} labeling in the DNA of cat cortex, but at a lesser rate than into RNA, which led him to suggest moderate DNA turnover.

Further work by Altman (1963*a*) showed labeling in the glial cells of rats and cats. Neurons with apparently labeled nuclei were observed in the midline cortex bilaterally and in the dentate gyrus of the hippocampus in both animals.

Altman (1963*b*) has used the autoradiographic procedure to investigate protein uptake of tritiated leucine in nerve cells during exercise. Four groups of two rats were used. One group was unstimulated; the three other groups were exercised in a motor driven wheel for two hours. One of these three groups was spun at 7 rpm and injected intraperitoneally with tritiated leucine after exercise. The second group was spun at 7 rpm but injected during the exercise. The last group was rotated at 12 rpm and injected after exercise. The group rotated at 7 rpm and injected during exercise showed the greatest uptake of leucine in the motor neurons in the lumbar and cervical portion of the spinal cord. The other exercised groups did not show a consistently greater uptake than did the nonstimulated animals.

The uptake of radioactive leucine in fifteen brain and spinal cord regions in nonstimulated animals was compared to that in the rats exercised at 7 rpm and injected during exercise. The greatest increase for the exercised group was in the motor structures, 49 to 66 per cent (Table 8-X). The visual area of the posterior cortex showed a 47 per cent increase. These results and others discussed above show the great lability of chemicals in the motor area.

The use of radiography as a qualitative indicator of activity sites is a valuable tool; its use for quantitative purposes is less

TABLE 8-X
PER CENT INCREASE IN LABELING IN BRAIN STRUCTURES OF
EXERCISED RATS OVER NONEXERCISED RATS
(Altman, 1963 *b*)

Structure	*% Increases*
Motor cortex, neurons in layer 2	66
Cervical cord, ventral horn cells	57
Motor cortex, pyramidal neurons in layer 5	49
Posterior cortex, layer 2 cells	47
Cervical cord, ventral horn cells	41
Posterior cortex, layer 5 cells	36
Lumbar cord, ventral horn cells	35
Mammillary body, neurons	34
Cerebellum, Purkinje cells	34
Medulla, large reticular neurons	32
Choroid plexus (3rd ventricle)	28
Hippocampus, pyramidal neurons	26
Deiter's nucleus, neurons	25
Hippocampus, granule cells	24
Cochlear nucleus, neurons	19

definitive. For example, assume that one is interested in RNA synthesis in brain sites A and B and both showed 500 counts/minute/g of tissue. This does not necessarily mean that both sites show the same activity. If brain site A has an RNA content of 700 $\mu g/g$ of tissue whereas only 200 $\mu g/g$ of RNA is present in site B, it is obvious that a greater number of counts/unit RNA is available in site B. Likewise, it is possible that membrane permeabilities vary in the different sites of concern, allowing differential amounts of the radioactive label to enter the cells. Thus for effective quantitative use of radiography one should obtain as much information as possible concerning the content of the various chemicals involved in the synthetic steps and cellular conditions. Unfortunately, it is rather difficult to obtain all this information. A suitable compromise procedure would be to supplement radiographic procedures with ones which would allow the determination of amounts of the chemical of concern. For example, with RNA one would determine the number of counts/minute/g of RNA.

In spite of these considerations, the above radiographic results are suggestive. The Altman results suggest that protein turnover is greater during stimulation and exercise which is what one would expect. RNA amounts would probably be greater during the stimulation and exercise as well, as other data discussed above show. Likewise, the Palladin and Vladimirov results are consistent with those from other methods.

The discussion of enzyme induction and hormonal activation would also be pertinent here. Thus there are many examples indicating that RNA amounts and activity (and proteins and phospholipids as well) increase during the functional activity of cells.

An important question raised by Pevzner (1966) is whether the RNA changes are primary or secondary events in neural function. He cites studies by Brodsky concerning the temporal interrelationship between nucleic acid metabolism and physiological processes in retinal neurons. Light adaptation processes in retinal ganglion cells during the change from darkness to light occur much sooner than the increase in cytoplasmic RNA amounts in these neurons. Brodsky also found that even though nuclear RNA changes occur prior to those of cytoplasmic RNA, the former lag behind the changes in neuron functional states. Brodsky concluded that the changes in RNA content probably reflect a secondary process and hence the physiological activity of the neuron is directly based on some other neurochemical reactions. Yet it is possible that the RNA changes may be both primary and secondary in nature, depending on the circumstances which are involved. The RNA changes may be primary in the early development of learning and other events but secondary after these events are well developed. For example, in a learning event RNA involvement may be required for protein and other chemical reactions to occur so that memory may be developed in some neurochemical fashion. After the memory is developed, however, the RNA involvement may be secondary to the other neurochemical processes. This possibility would be suggesting that RNA changes are primary when *changes in function* are involved but secondary when *function* is of concern.

INSTINCTIVE BEHAVIOR AND IMPRINTING

These behaviors represent more complex events than those discussed in the two previous sections but less complex than those to be considered in Chapter 9. Instinctive behavior involves a complex behavioral sequence which proceeds in a relatively stereotyped manner. As Morgan indicated, however, instinctive behavior is not easily defined. The term instinct has been applied rather loosely and at one point the category became so broad as to be meaningless. In recent years the term has been used to refer to behavior patterns that (1) are innate or develop through maturation; (2) are species specific, being found in all members of a species, and (3) are released by specific patterns of stimulation (Morgan, 1965).

An example of instinctive behavior is the migration of salmon. Breeding normally takes place in small streams which constitute the headwaters of major rivers. Later the young move down the river into the sea. Some years later they migrate back to the river and up to the headwaters for breeding, quite frequently to the same stream in which they were hatched.

The causative factors involved in either direction of migration are not known. Morgan (1965) thought that the fish might use the sun as a compass for navigation and that their ability to return to the home stream was guided by distinctive chemical cues within the stream. He indicated that the precision of the salmons' returning to the same stream in which they were hatched suggested the operation of some kind of memory, possibly imprinting, and not instinctive selection of streams.

Other behaviors which are included within the instinctive behavior category are hibernation, hoarding in some animals, nest building, copulation in certain animals and caring for young. Underlying these complex behavioral sequences are presumably neurological and biochemical events. However, little is known about these factors. The author is aware of no research which has investigated nucleic acid structure and/or function during these behaviors. Probably specific environmental events set off physiological reactions in the organism, resulting in the activation of one or more gene sites with RNA and protein synthesis, and multiple other neurological events, occurring. Possibly hormones may be involved in gene activation in similar fashion as insect chromosomal activation by ecdysone discussed in Chapter 6. An event such as hibernation may involve a reverse result, the deactivation of gene sites.

The distinction between instinctive behavior and imprinting is not clear cut. Some examples of imprinting would be included in the instinctive category by certain individuals, e.g., migration of fishes by Morgan (1965) as indicated above. Because the two categories historically developed separately, they will be so treated here.

The term imprinting refers to a rapid learning event which occurs at a very early period in the life of an organism. The tendency of certain birds to follow and form an emotional attachment to the first moving object they perceive after birth is the most common example that has been investigated. Ordinarily the parent is the object to which the attachment is formed; however, numerous individuals (e.g., Hess, 1964; Klopfer, 1965) indicated attachment to any moving objects, even an inanimate one. There is a "critical period" in which this experience develops. For example, Hess reported that in chicks and ducklings the period lasts up to thirty-two or thirty-six hours after hatching, with the peak of sensitivity occurring at thirteen to sixteen hours of age in both species.

Again little is known of the neurological and biochemical events which underlie imprinting. One study by Beckwith (1962) indicated that the degree of following by chicks (New Hampshire Red Chicken) was inversely related to the amount of RNA in the brain, i.e., the greater the RNA the less the tendency to imprint. Beckwith interpreted the results as indicating that the greater the RNA supply the less susceptible was the bird to develop this rigid type of learning. However, this interpretation may be confusing cause and effect. The lesser amounts of RNA in birds who show greater following may merely show that RNA utilization and degradation has occurred. As indicated in the previous section, mild stimulation brings about an increase in RNA content whereas greater activation can result in decreased amounts.

Molecular events operative in imprinting are probably similar to those in instinctive behavior. Possibly one or more gene sites are activated by appropriate environmental cues, i.e., a moving object. RNA and protein synthesis would be important intermediary steps with numerous other neurochemical events ensuing.

CHAPTER 9

RESEARCH AND THEORIZING FOR COMPLEX BEHAVIORAL EVENTS — LEARNING AND MEMORY

POSSIBLE NUCLEIC ACID MECHANISMS

THE EXACT MECHANISMS WHEREBY the organism encodes or represents his life experiences are obscure. The research concerning the role of the nucleic acids in translating genetic information into physical mechanisms (protein synthesis) suggests a number of possible ways in which the memory underlying learning events can be developed. If one or both of the nucleic acids are going to function uniquely in experiential events the representation or involvement must be via either primary, secondary, tertiary or quaternary structures which have been discussed in Chapter 5.

Primary, Secondary, and Tertiary Structures

In that the linear sequence of bases in DNA contains the basic genetic information which is transferred to messenger RNA, it appeared plausible a few years ago to suggest that the linear sequence of bases in brain DNA or in one of the RNA fractions in the brain might represent the experiential code. The stimulation afforded by the environment would precipitate nerve impulses which under the appropriate intracellular conditions would result in a change in the DNA or RNA base sequence. This would be considered an "instructive" type of representation (qualitative change), i.e., new molecules are made which differ in base sequences from the previous ones. If DNA were to be changed in base sequences, then the RNA's and proteins developed from this DNA template would be modified, likewise. Thus one would expect to find different RNA's and proteins in brain tissue where learning occurs than in other tissues such as liver and kidney which are not involved directly in learning.

Likewise, if RNA were to be modified, one would expect different proteins synthesized in the brain than elsewhere. This type of mechanism, either with RNA or DNA, was the favorite mechanism for most theorists at first (e.g., Dingman and Sporn, 1961; Gaito, 1961; Hyden, 1959).

Modification of the hydrogen bonding across helices (secondary structure) might be invoked to represent experiential events. For example, base units on an RNA might dissociate from a bond with one base and link with another elsewhere on the strand.

Modification of the overall configuration of a nucleic acid might be suggested as a possible mechanism also. Both the modification in secondary and tertiary structures would be of an "instructive" nature if the changes resulted in new molecules being synthesized. However, this event would be of "selective" nature if there occurred a change in the rate of synthesis of molecules which are present, or potentially present, already. For example, Nirenberg (1963) indicated that with increasing amounts of secondary structure of messenger RNA (which would change the tertiary structure as well) is associated decreased degrees of protein synthesis. Thus a change in secondary and/or tertiary structure might affect protein synthesis and thereby cell functioning in behaviour.

Quaternary Structure

Rather than looking to the primary, secondary, or tertiary structures for a means of handling learning and memory, one could consider changes in nucleic acid complexes which would effect the function of the nucleic acid involved, e.g., modification of histones complexed with DNA. The models underlying regulator and operator genes (enzyme induction) and hormonal activation would be pertinent here also.

Such a means of handling memory events would be of selective nature in that no new molecules are synthesized beyond those which are specified genetically (quantitative changes). However, it is possible that molecules can be synthesized which have not been synthesized before. For example, assume that the histone-DNA complex is responsible for learning events. During the first learning event of the organism the stimulation via nerve impulses could loosen histones complexed with specific DNA segments and allow messenger RNA's homologous to those segments to be synthesized. This event would result in the synthesis of a protein which had not been present previously. The effect on the histones could be of such nature that the inhibitory effect on those DNA sites would be less than previously and the synthesis of messenger RNA's might be effected more easily thereafter. Or the change may be transient ones effective only during the stimulation events and then return to an equilibrium state would occur. In this connection, Allfrey, Faulkner and Mirsky (1964) have suggested a relatively minor modification of histone, reversible in nature, as offering a means of switching on and off RNA synthesis at different loci along the chromosomes. They found that acetylation of the arginine rich histone complex decreased the inhibitory effect on RNA synthesis from 60-75 per cent down to zero in calf thymus nuclei. Similar reduction in inhibition occurred with *E. coli*, a decrease from 47.6 per cent to 22.0 per cent upon acetylation of histones.

The quaternary structure models are more plausible than the others and appear to be more consistent with molecular biological data. However, the exact neurochemical events in the overall sequence underlying learning phenomena are unknown.

EXPERIMENTAL DATA

Studies Concerned with RNA Base Composition

Holger Hyden of Sweden has been the pioneer in attempting to relate RNA to behavioral events. His publications on this subject are numerous but only a few will be considered here. Some of his work has been summarized in Chapter 8. He demonstrated that RNA and proteins are produced in the nerve cells at a rate which follows the neuronal activity (1959, 1961). He suggested that the nerve cell fulfills its function under a steady and rapidly changing production of proteins, with the RNA as an activator and governing molecule; he hypothesized that memory involves a change in the sequence of bases in the RNA molecule; this change occurs when one or more bases are exchanged with the surrounding cytoplasmic materials.

Hyden and Egyhazi (1962) exposed young rats to a situation in which they had to balance on a wire to reach a platform where food was located. The only way for the animals to satisfy their hunger was to accomplish this exceedingly difficult task. The rats took an average of four days of forty-five-minute sessions to balance on the wire the total distance to the food platform. Four days later they were visiting the platform an average of twenty times within the allotted forty-five minutes. The animals were then sacrificed and Deiter nerve cells from the vestibular nucleus of the medulla were dissected. Control rats remained in the home cages. Functional controls were provided by rotating animals through 120° horizontally and 30° vertically with thirty turns per minute for two periods of twenty-five minutes on each of four days. The average amount of RNA per cell was: controls, 683 micromicrograms ($\mu\mu$g); functional controls, 722 $\mu\mu$g; and experimentals, 751 $\mu\mu$g. From these results there is the implication that a greater amount of stimulation was involved in the "learning" task than for the functional controls. However, the qualitatively different stimulation for the functional controls may be responsible for the difference.

Hyden and Egyhazi investigated also the base composition of the RNA extracted. They found that the cytoplasmic RNA of controls was no different than that of the experimentals (Table 9-I). In nuclear RNA, there were significant differences in base ratios. In the experimental group there was a greater amount of A and lesser amounts of U than in the other two groups (Table 9-II).

TABLE 9-I

MEAN PERCENT BASE COMPOSITION OF CYTOPLASMIC RNA FROM DEITERS CELLS FOR EXPERIMENTAL AND CONTROL RATS
(Hyden and Egyhazi, 1962)

Bases	*Controls*	*Experimentals*
Adenine	20.5	20.9
Guanine	33.7	34.0
Cytosine	27.4	26.8
Uracil	18.4	18.3

TABLE 9-II

MEAN PERCENT BASE COMPOSITION OF NUCLEAR RNA FROM DEITERS CELLS FOR EXPERIMENTAL AND CONTROL RATS
(Hyden and Egyhazi, 1962)

Bases	*Controls*	*Functional* *Controls*	*Experimentals*
Adenine	21.4	21.3	24.1
Guanine	26.2	25.7	26.7
Cytosine	31.9	31.9	31.0
Uracil	20.5	21.7	18.2

The authors maintained that the results indicated the change of RNA bases during learning.

Hyden and Egyhazi (1963) did a similar experiment but were concerned mainly with glial RNA. In previous experiments differences had been indicated in base amounts in nerve and glial cells of non-stimulated control animals. The glial RNA showed higher A and lower G values than nerve cell RNA (Table 9-III). "Learning" animals showed an increase in the A to U ratio (somewhat similar to the change in nerve cells reported in the previous experiment) but no change in base composition resulted for the functional controls (Table 9-IV). A significant decrease in C was observed for the "learning" animals. Nuclear RNA in nerve cells of a functional control group that was rotated 120° vertically increased about 25 to 30 per cent; however, no change in base composition resulted.

TABLE 9-III
MEAN PERCENT BASE COMPOSITION OF GLIAL AND NERVE CELL
RNA OF CONTROL RATS
(Hyden and Egyhazi, 1963)

Bases	Nerve Cells	Glia
Adenine	20.5	25.3
Guanine	33.7	29.0
Cytosine	27.4	26.5
Uracil	18.4	19.2

TABLE 9-IV
MEAN PERCENT BASE COMPOSITION OF GLIAL RNA FOR
EXPERIMENTAL AND CONTROL RATS
(Hyden and Egyhazi, 1963)

Bases	Controls	Functional Controls	Experimentals
Adenine	25.3	25.1	28.3
Guanine	29.0	28.6	28.8
Cytosine	26.5	27.4	24.3
Uracil	19.2	18.9	18.6

Hyden and Egyhazi also dissected nerve cells from the reticular formation in the medulla and extracted nuclear RNA. The average amount of RNA per nerve cell during a four day learning period was: Day 1, 515 $\mu\mu$g; Day 2, 568 $\mu\mu$g; Day 3, 568 $\mu\mu$g; and Day 4, 590 $\mu\mu$g. There were, however, no significant differences in base composition for control and "learning" animals (Table 9-V).

TABLE 9-V
MEAN PERCENT BASE COMPOSITION OF NEURAL RNA
FROM RETICULAR FORMATION
(Hyden and Egyhazi, 1963)

Bases	Controls	Experimentals
Adenine	23.9	22.8
Guanine	25.3	26.2
Cytosine	28.9	29.7
Uracil	21.9	21.3

Hyden and Egyhazi (1963) also reported that during development of Parkinson's disorder, changes in RNA base ratios of the glia were found to precede in time similar changes in nerve cells in the globus pallidus.

From these experiments they concluded that gene sites in chromosomes of neurons were induced to synthesize RNA with specific base ratios concomitantly in both neurons and glia in the "learning" experiments. They suggested that the glia and glial RNA constitute the substrate for short-term memory since the folded membranes of the glia would be very suited for rapid processes and that the neurons and its mass of RNA could then house the substrate for long-term memory.

Hyden (1964) compared the RNA content and composition of globus pallidus neurons and neuroglia of patients with Parkinson's disease with material taken from cases of sudden death of persons with no abnormal symptoms. The globus pallidus is a subcortical structure which is involved in this disorder. The RNA in both the neurons and glia of the Parkinson patients was greater than in the controls, 116 and 17 $\mu\mu$g per cell for the neurons and neuroglia, respectively for the controls and 145 and 34 for the Parkinson's disease cases. Both the nerve cells and glia of Parkinson's disease patients showed different base composition than the controls (Table 9-VI). In neurons the Parkinson's disease cases showed increased A and decreased G values. Similar changes occurred in the glia but were of greater magnitude. Also U showed a significant decrease.

Another interesting experiment involving the forcing of right-handed rats to use the left hand to obtain food was conducted by Hyden and Egyhazi (1964). The RNA of neurons from layers 5 and 6 of a small sector of the anterior dorsal cortex was obtained.

TABLE 9-VI
BASE COMPOSITION IN MOLAR PERCENTAGES FOR
GLOBUS PALLIDUS NEURONS AND NEUROGLIA OF PARKINSON'S
DISEASE CASES AND CONTROL PATIENTS
(Hyden, 1964)

Bases	Controls Neurons Glia		Parkinson's Disaese Neurons Glia	
Adenine	18.3	19.0	20.7	30.8
Guanine	30.5	29.1	28.8	20.3
Cytosine	35.3	33.7	34.4	33.2
Uracil	15.9	18.2	16.1	15.7

Tissue was obtained both from the left hemisphere controlling the right hand (control) and right hemisphere involved in the "learning" task (experimental). This procedure allowed for each animal to be his own control. A significant difference occurred, 22 $\mu\mu$g/cell for controls compared to 27 $\mu\mu$g/cell for the "learning" side. Changes in base ratios also resulted (Table 9-VII) with A, G and U increasing and C decreasing. Three right-handed animals not involved in the transfer experiments were analyzed with respect to content and composition of RNA from the same neurons as analyzed in the transfer experiment. No significant difference between right and left sides of the hemisphere was found. In another experiment three right-handed rats were allowed to perform the same number of reaches and for the same time as the animals in the learning experiment. A slight increase of RNA in the left side neurons occurred but no base changes resulted.

TABLE 9-VII
RNA BASE COMPOSITION OF CORTICAL NEURONS OF LEFT SIDE
(CONTROL) AND RIGHT SIDE (EXPERIMENTAL)
(Hyden and Egyhazi, 1964)

Base	Controls	Experimentals
Adenine	18.4	20.1
Guanine	26.5	28.7
Cytosine	36.8	31.5
Uracil	18.3	19.6

The interesting aspect of Hyden's results are the base changes. However, the meaning of these changes is not clear. Two major alternatives are suggested. A qualitative change may be occurring with polymer RNA being modified to produce a new molecular species or foreign RNA may permeate certain cells such that the

RNA population contains new types of RNA. On the other hand, quantitative changes may be involved, i.e., the relative amounts of the species of transfer, ribosomal, and messenger RNA's may be changing. The latter possibility appears to be the most likely one.

Studies Involving Administration of RNA, RNA Constituents, or RNase

Further evidence relative to the involvement of RNA in behavior is provided by the results of Cameron and Solyom (1961) of McGill University. They found that administration of RNA (but not DNA) to aged individuals brought about memory improvement. These changes involved almost total retention in some cases. When the RNA was discontinued later, memory relapses occurred.

A similar study with rats was conducted by Cook *et al.* (1963) ; they injected doses of RNA in rats for three days, one week, two weeks and one month. The rats were placed in a chamber with an electrified grid floor, a pole suspended from the top center, and a buzzer. They were given trials in which the buzzer and shock through the grid floor were presented simultaneously. Later only the buzzer was presented. Each trial was terminated by jumping onto the pole after the onset of the buzzer (conditioned response) or at the end of thirty seconds. The authors reported that the RNA groups were superior to control groups in the acquisition of avoidance responses in all except the three day interval; however, resistance to extinction was greater in the RNA groups for all time periods.

The improvements in these RNA experiments may have occurred because RNA or its constituents may provide necessary metabolites for the metabolic pool and thus influence the overall performance of the organism, not affecting memory alone; for the ribonucleotides, or portions of the nucleotides, are constituents of numerous cellular products such as ATP, GTP, UTP, CTP, a number of coenzymes and phospholipids which are essential for normal neural function. For example, A nucleotides play an important role in energy metabolism; C nucleotides participate in the synthesis of lipids; nucleotides of U and G take part in the synthesis of polysaccharides; and G nucleotides function in the synthesis of proteins (Mandel and Harth, 1961). Such general effects were reported by Sved and Kral (1963). This possibility is suggested also by investigators in Italy (cited by Cameron *et al.*, 1962) who found behavioral improvement when the nucleotides of RNA were fed to memory deficient patients. Polymer RNA probably would be degraded before reaching the brain but mononucleotides would penetrate brain regions (Bonavita *et al.*, 1963).

That polymer RNA or its constituents is related to general cellular requirements is also suggested by the *in vitro* studies of Rounds and Slick (1963). They reported that a twenty-four hour preirradiation treatment of an amnion cell line with yeast RNA increased cell survival in proportion to the yeast RNA content in the medium. Some increase in cell survival was recorded when mononucleotides of yeast RNA were used. Cell survival potential decreased when RNase was added to the medium.

Further support for the suggestion that a general metabolic effect may occur which is extraneous to memory functioning is provided by the results of Weiss and Sokoloff (1963). It has been known for years that cellular metabolism varies directly with the levels of thyroxine. Weiss and Sokoloff indicated a direct relationship between thyroxine and protein synthesis. They inhibited protein synthesis in thyrotoxic rats with puromycin and the metabolic rate decreased. These results suggested that the effect of thyroxine on metabolism was secondary to the effect on protein synthesis. From this indication that protein synthesis is related to metabolism, it follows that variation in RNA synthesis (which affects protein synthesis) may modify metabolism and thus have a general effect on behavior.

Further memory improvement results have been reported by other researchers at McGill University (Kral and Sved, 1963). They also indicated that the RNase activity in the blood increases with age. They suggested that the yeast RNA administered to the elderly patients in their studies was attacked by the RNase and this event allowed more of the native RNA of the human to be free from attack.

It has been reported by Thompson and McConnell (1955) that the planarian, a flatworm, is capable of acquiring a conditioned response (contraction to light following a series of trials in which light and shock are paired). When cut in half following conditioning the worm will regenerate head and tail animals which show "memory" for the previous conditioning as indicated by requiring fewer trials to reach a criterion in later conditioning training. Corning and John (1961) conditioned a number of flatworms and then transected them into head and tail sections. They thought that RNA might play a role in the transmission of an acquired structural configuration from the trained to the regenerating tissues. Thus they reasoned that if the trained portions were regenerated in the presence of RNase the enzyme would affect the altered RNA structure producing some animals with a naive head and trained tails and others with trained heads and naive tails. They stated that the head region would probably be dominant and thus the trained head animals should show more retention. They reported that heads regenerated in RNase retained the "memory" as well as did head and tail sections regenerating in pond water but the tails regenerating in RNase performed randomly. The authors suggested that the RNase did not affect intact tissue but did interfere with regenerating tissue and maintained that the results are compatible with the assumption that RNA is involved in memory events.

Zelman et al. (1963) trained planaria in a classic conditioning situation. Then RNA was extracted from these worms and from untrained worms. The "sophisticated" RNA was injected in one group of planaria and "naive" RNA into another group. They found some tendency, but not a consistent one, for the animals fed "sophisticated" RNA to respond more frequently to the conditioned stimulus than did the animals fed "naive" RNA.

A similar experiment was conducted by Fjerdingstad et al. (1965) using rats. They obtained RNA preparations from animals which had been conditioned in a simple maze and from nonconditioned rats. They then injected intracisternaly the "sophisticated" RNA in one group of animals. The same volume (but not necessarily the same amount) of "naive" RNA (50 μl/animal) was injected in another group. A third group consisted of uninjected controls. The group injected with "sophisticated" RNA was significantly superior in maze performance in two test sessions of about fifteen reinforcements each and in later trials. Jacobsen *et al.* (1966) reported also a facilitative effect by an RNA extract from trained rats on later performance of naive rats in a two choice discrimination task.

Other studies show negative results. In a number of RNA injection experiments, Halstead (personal communication) has not found a facilitative effect consistently. No facilitation was obtained by Gross and Carey (1965) in two experiments utilizing RNA injections. Furthermore, Ungar and Navarro (1965) obtained results which suggested that protein, rather than RNA, was the agent responsible for facilitation. They extracted brain tissues from sound habituated mice and injected these into naive mice. The recipient animals habituated to sound sooner than rats who had received an extract from untrained rats. When they treated the brain etxract with chymotrypsin, a proteolytic agent, prior to injection no facilitation occurred. If the extract was incubated with RNase, the facilitation effect was still present. Other chemical reactions suggested also that the component responsible for the facilitation was protein.*

These results are interesting but leave many questions unanswered. It would be desirable in studies of this nature to include biochemical analyses of polymer RNA and nucleotides, nucleosides and bases in the cell pool; these procedures could be supplemented by determining the radioactivity of RNA components both in polymer RNA and in the cell pool. These results could then be related to the behavioral modifications for a clearer picture of cellular events. The analysis of RNA constituents in the cell pool probably will yield significant information. Presumably general metabolic events of the cell are affected by the injected chemicals.

Studies Involving Administration of Chemicals Which Affect RNA Synthesis

Dingman and Sporn (1961) performed two experiments with radioactive 8-azaguanine injections in rats. Eight-azaguanine was used as an inhibitor of RNA because this base analogue had been shown to be an inhibitor of enzyme synthesis in bacteria. In both experiments chromatographic procedures indicated that the base analogue had been incorporated into the RNA of the brain. In

---

*More recently Luttges *et al.* (1966) reported negative results in a series of experiments with several tasks under many conditions.

neither experiment was there any significant difference between experimental and control animals in average time to run the maze, suggesting that 8-azaguanine had no adverse effect on the motor ability of the animals. However, in one experiment the experimental animals had a significantly greater mean number of errors than did the controls on all fifteen trials in the learning of a maze. In another experiment concerned with retention of a maze pattern (tested by a single trial after learning a maze), experimental animals did not differ significantly from control animals, even though the experimental animals had a greater average number of errors than did the control animals. There were only eight animals used in each group (as compared with fourteen and fifteen in the learning experiment); thus it is possible that if n had been larger in the retention experiment the power of the statistical test would have been greater and the results would have indicated that 8-azaguanine adversely affects both learning and retention of maze patterns in rats.

Based on their results, Dingman and Sporn maintained that RNA may be directly involved in learning but not in retention. However, they admitted that their results did not necessarily indicate that RNA metabolism was intimately linked with the formation of memory traces in the brain because 8-azaguanine might have interfered with metabolic processes which affected RNA indirectly.

Gerard (1963) and Chamberlain, Rothschild, and Gerard (1963) reported that when RNA synthesis was hastened by malononitrile, avoidance learning was facilitated but no effect was noted on maze behavior. 8-azaguanine had no effect on either avoidance conditioning or maze behavior.

Studies Concerned with DNA Base Composition

Most researchers seem to have favored RNA as being uniquely involved in memory events. The possibility that DNA is directly involved in memory events has been rejected by all but a few individuals.

If the primary structure of DNA of the brain were modified during learning, the base amounts of brain DNA should be different than that in nonneural tissues. Kit (1961) found that the base composition from the whole brain of mice, monkeys and alligators was the same as DNA base composition from other tissues. However, DNA changes might occur in the cortex of an animal during experience but be undetected if confounded with unchanged DNA in the remaining portions of the brain.

Gaito performed a study in 1963 (unpublished) which involved a comparison of the DNA in the cortex and other neural tissue with that in liver and kidneys of dogs and rats. Two stray mongrel dogs, approximately one year of age were sacrificed, and liver, kidneys and cortex (from frontal and temporal lobes) were removed. The DNA was extracted by a modification of the Kirby phenol procedure (1958). Four Sprague-Dawley rats from a single litter were also studied. Two animals (experimentals) lived together from twenty-eight days of age in a cage which contained small wooden blocks for manipulation experience. These animals were housed in the main animal room and were able to see, hear, and smell other animals. Each weekend they were taken to the home of the experimenter and provided with varying stimulation. This included exploring and learning a one unit T maze pattern, being handled by children and playing with a large dog.

Two other rats (controls) of the same age were isolated in a single dark room in separate shielded cages. They were able to hear and smell each other and two other isolated rats. They had no wooden objects in their cages nor were they given any special stimulation. They received visual stimulation for a few minutes three times a week when fresh food and water were provided and debris removed. They had adequate food and water at all times. At no time were the control animals handled.

The animals were sacrificed at eight months of age and the liver, kidneys and brain were extracted quickly; the brain was sectioned into cortex, cerebral hemispheres less the cortex, brain stem, and cerebellum. The Schmidt-Thannheuser procedure (Leslie, 1955) was utilized for extraction of DNA. One DNA sample for each tissue from each rat was obtained; two DNA samples for each tissue were obtained with one dog but only one sample with the second one.

The purines (A and G) were obtained by hydrolysis. Table 9-VIII shows the molar percentage of A for both dogs and rats.

The amount of G is equal to 50 per cent minus the amount of A and the amounts of T and C are equal to the amounts of A and G, respectively. Statistical analyses indicated that the base amounts of various tissues within the dogs and rats were not significantly different. Likewise, no significant differences between experimental and control animals were indicated. The observed values are consistent with those reported in the literature; the A in DNA of animal tissues varies around 30 per cent for many species (Sueoka, 1961).

TABLE 9-VIII
MEAN MOLAR PERCENTAGES OF ADENINE IN
VARIOUS TISSUES OF DOGS AND RATS

	*Dogs**	*Rats* Experimentals	Controls
Cortex	30.4 (1.2) **	32.4 (1.5)	29.8 (0.2)
Cerebral Hemispheres		31.5 (0.3)	31.4 (0.3)
Cerebellum		29.6 (1.9)	31.4 (1.3)
Brain Stem		32.7 (0.2)	31.8 (2.0)
Liver	31.0 (1.2)	29.9 (1.4)	29.8 (2.6)
Kidneys	31.6 (0.9)	30.2 (1.1)	29.7 (1.4)

*Three samples for each of the dog tissues; two samples of each tissue for both experimental and control rats.
**Standard deviations in parentheses.

These negative results suggest that the primary structure of brain DNA is not involved in experiential coding. However, an undesirable feature of this procedure is that a change could occur in one portion of the nucleic acid and if the reverse change transpired elsewhere, the overall result on base ratios would be nil. For example, A might change to G at one site, and G to A at another site. Another undesirable feature is that the molecular change may be so small as to obviate its being detected by these procedures. Thus these results must be considered as inconclusive. However, as has been indicated above, the author believes that one of the quaternary structures of DNA is the most plausible candidate for involvement in learning events.

Studies Using Protein Inhibitors

Flexner, Flexner and Stellar (1963) injected a protein synthesis inhibitor, puromycin, into the brain of mice at various time periods following the acquisition of an avoidance discrimination response (moving into a shock free arm of a Y maze within five seconds). The anatomical spread of puromycin was checked with control injections of fluorescein in a number of animals. Some animals received frontal injections; others, temporal injections; and others, ventricular injections. Injections in two and three areas were employed also with some animals .

All injections were of bilateral nature. They reported that injections after one day involving the hippocampus and adjacent temporal cortices caused loss of memory. Loss of memory following injections after twelve days or longer required injections in all three areas. Other results suggested that spread of the memory trace from the temporal area to wide areas of the cortex required three to six days. They also found that recent reversal learning was lost with bilateral injections in the hippocampal-temporal areas but longer term initial learning was retained.

In a later study Flexner *et al.* (1964) found that protein synthesis in both the hippocampus and temporal cortex must be inhibited for at least eight to ten hours in excess of 80 per cent for loss of recent memory of maze learning to occur. Bilateral temporal injections of puromycin achieved this degree and duration of inhibition and consistently caused loss of memory. As the concentration of the antibiotic was decreased, it became progressively less effective in its behavioral and biochemical effects so that recent memory was retained in an increasing proportion of animals as the effect on protein synthesis diminished. Subcutaneous injections of varying amounts of another protein synthesis inhibitor, chloramphenicol, did not cause 80 per cent inhibition and none of the mice showed loss or impairment of memory.

Flexner *et al.* (1965) reported that longer term memory could be destroyed in a majority of mice by injections which inhibited protein synthesis in the hippocampus and temporal cortex by at least 80 per cent for eleven hours and in a substantial part of the remaining cortex for the same time period. As the concentration of the inhibitor decreased it became progressively less effective, and the longer term memory was retained in an increasing number of animals as the effect on protein synthesis diminished. They suggested that the maintenance of memory may depend upon a continuing synthesis of protein.

Puromycin injected intracranially in goldfish also produced impairment of memory for a shock avoidance response (Agranoff and Klinger, 1964). If the goldfish were ovetrained, puromycin caused no impairment of memory. Contrary to the results of the Flexner group, Agranoff reported that puromycin injections beyond ninety minutes after the last learning trial had no effect on memory (personal communication). The Flexner group found memory impairment with injections one to three days after learning had occurred. The differences are probably related to the different complexity of brain structures in the two species with a longer time period required for memory to be stabilized in the mouse brain.

These results suggest that protein is an important component for the memory process; they also imply that DNA activity with associated RNA increases would possibly be involved for the protein synthesis. The RNA increases need not be required, however; the RNA responsible for protein synthesis might be of long-lived nature.

NEUROCHEMICAL HYPOTHESES, MODELS AND THEORIES CONCERNED WITH LEARNING PHENOMENA

Holger Hyden has been the pioneer in proposing and evaluating the hypothesis that RNA is of basic importance in learning. His work of more than a decade is summarized in an excellent article in *Scientific American* (1961). He has developed some amazing dissection, extraction and analytic procedures; he dissects single nerve cells quickly and is able to extract and analyze RNA in amounts as small as 45 $\mu\mu$g. These procedures represent a very significant contribution to biological science.

At first, Hyden advocated a qualitative change type theory (1959, 1961) but his recent work suggests that he has shifted to an emphasis on quantitative changes, although this is not clearly stated. It is even possible that his recent ideas incorporate both qualitative and quantitative aspects. We will look at his ideas in detail.

In his early theory, he hypothesized that memory involves a change in the sequence of bases in the RNA molecule through frequency modulation; one or more bases are exchanged with the surrounding cytoplasmic materials. The details of the formation of the memory trace are as follows.

1) SPECIFICATION OF RNA IN THE NERVE CELL. The first series of impulses generated in sensory cells or in motor neurons pre-or postnatally change the stability of one or more of the four bases of the RNA molecule at a certain site along the molecule. Precisely which changes in stability will occur depend on the modulated frequency of the first series of impulses generated in the nerve cell. This effects a change of one against another base from the surrounding pool. The new base at this space is now stable under the influence of the modulated frequency. The new pattern remains and constitutes the specification of the RNA in the nerve cell.

2) FORMATION OF NEW PROTEIN. Since the sequence of the bases in the template RNA is now changed, new protein formed through the mediation of the RNA will also be specified.

3) DISSOCIATION OF PROTEIN. Stimulation causes a rapid dissociation of the specified protein and the combination of the dissociated products with a complementary molecule or an energy activation of the specified dissociated protein.

4) ACTIVATION OF TRANSMITTER SUBSTANCE. Through a rapid combination of the dissociated protein with a complementary molecule in the third step, an activation occurs of the transmitter substance, and the postsynaptic structure is excited.

Hyden held that the neurons are interconnected in complex tridimensional chains. Thus when neurons in an already established memory trace are activated, regardless of how many there are, or where they are located the hypothesis implies the reaction consists of the rapid third and fourth steps in the scheme. The impulses in the form of modulated frequencies activate the specified protein and release the transmitter substance causing the next neuron in the chain to be activated or excited. The transmitter substance may be ACh or any assumed inhibitory substance.

Hyden apparently agreed with some type of Hebbian approach regarding the linking of cells to form chains or circuits in that he maintained that the reason that only neurons of a chain respond is because protein, once specified by a modulated frequency, responds to the same electrical pattern whenever repeated but will not react to other patterns.

In Hyden's system strict localization of function in the brain is not required. The same neuron could participate as a link in many neuronal networks, depending on the response of the sequence of the bases in the RNA to the modulated frequency. Association might grow out of successive specification of neurons.

Hyden's early theory may be summarized in less technical terms as follows. A nerve cell responds differentially depending on whether the pattern of impulses it receives is novel or familiar, as well as on the pattern itself. No protein will have the correct configuration if the incoming pattern of impulses is new; therefore, no dissociation of protein (followed by transmitter substance explosion) can occur. The electrical pattern must first shape a new RNA molecule, which in turn shapes a protein molecule that can dissociate. The molecule fragments and then reacts with a complementary molecule, causing the triggering of a substance (excitatory or inhibitory) across the synapse. If, on the other hand, the incoming impulse is familiar, protein molecules will already be present that are capable of dissociating rapidly. Each cell may perpetuate within itself a large number of unique patterns of RNA and protein. A giant RNA molecule could accommodate along its length many different sequences shaped by different impulse patterns that have coursed through the neuron.

Hyden (1962) maintained that increased stimulation caused a change of frequency in the neuron, thus effecting the release of specific nucleotides in the glia which were transferred to the neuron. These nucleotides blocked a repressor RNA in the neuron and enzyme induction and specific protein synthesis resulted.

In a more recent article (Hyden and Egyhazi, 1963) it was suggested that glia and glial RNA constitute the substrate for short-term memory whereas the neuron and its RNA would be the substrate of long-term memory. (See previous section). Thus for Hyden the glial RNA functions for short term memory and to derepress neuronal repressor RNA during enzyme induction.

Gaito (1961) suggested that changes might occur at the attachment of the two strands of DNA, with A at one locus changing to G and the associated pyrimidine changing from T to C. Deletion, addition, and rearrangement of bases could be other means of changing the code. Thus these changes would provide a basis for modification of the genetic potential in nerve cells by means of external stimulation during learning. This would be a somatic mutation which would not be transmitted to the offspring. However, other possible biochemical mechanisms were suggested which could be involved in memory functions, i.e., changes in RNA or amino acid sequences. The changes in RNA or amino acid sequences could occur either in the nucleus or cytoplasm of the nerve cell; DNA changes would occur in the nucleus. It is also possible that some of these modifications might occur in the cell processes, even at the synapse.

Dingman and Sporn (1961) hypothesized that RNA changes were the basis for memory. However, they suggested that the linear sequence of bases (primary structure) was only one possible means of codifying experimental events. They suggested that changes in the helical structure (secondary structure) and overall configuration (tertiary structure) could be the basis for memory.

Gerard (1963) proposed that RNA has a prominent role in establishing the memory trace. He suggested that the protein molecules formed by RNA would constitute the enduring trace. He also indicated that different or additional mechanisms might be involved in memories lasting more than an hour, in very ancient memories, and in memories which persist for a short period and then vanish, e.g., remembering a telephone number for a few seconds before completing the call.

McConnell (1964) presented a "tape recorder" theory in which RNA constituted the tape on which experience was recorded; the more RNA that an individual had, the more he could learn. He suggested that glial and neural RNA would be intimately involved in the recording and was not certain as to whether a "selectional" or "instructional" mechanism for recording was most appropriate.

Cameron (1963) suggested that RNA constitutes the substrate for memory and that a possible factor in memory disturbance may be overactivity of RNase.

Smith (1962) stated that the enzyme induction model could be suitable for learning events. He suggested that the inducer substance may be ACh which is released at the synapse during stimulation. The proteins then induced would be ChA and AChE. These events are presumed to increase the amounts of ACh at the synapse and increase the probability that stimulation in neural units will activate other neural units, thus leading to greater potential for adaptive behavior. Briggs and Kitto (1962) and Goldberg (1964) have expressed somewhat similar views. However, none of these individuals suggested the exact molecular events underlying repression and induction.

Gaito (1963a) reviewed the literature concerning the possible involvement of the nucleic acids in memory and concluded that there was no conclusive evidence to indicate that either DNA or RNA has a unique role in memory. He presented a number of reasons why RNA appeared not to have a unique role and suggested that DNA was important in learning events.

In a later paper (Gaito, 1963b), the author has presented further arguments against the RNA hypothesis. He suggested that quaternary structures (DNA complexes) appeared most plausible to account for learning phenomena. The emphasis was on the enzyme induction model and the inhibitory aspects of histone.

Using some of Hyden's results as a base, Landauer (1964) presented an interesting approach based on two hypotheses.

LEARNING HYPOTHESIS. Glial cells are specialized to provide RNA which will produce an alteration in neurons so that the neurons will become more sensitive to the events occurring in the brain when the RNA is produced. Only conducting neurons, i.e., stimulated neurons, will incorporate the RNA. The RNA produced would be associated with the conditioned stimulus (CS) attending the excitation of brain areas. Thus with stimulation of the organism during the operation of a CS, glial cells release an RNA which enters the neurons that are active at that time. The entering RNA would change the RNA population of the cell and its conductivity. The new RNA might act on the cell in a manner similar to that which occurs in the "transformation experiments," i.e., the nucleic acid is incorporated in the genome and produces an overall change in the organism. The ultimate result is a change in the protein synthesizing machinery of the neuron.

RETRIEVAL HYPOTHESIS. Conditioning results in a change of sensitivity of a neuron to some characteristic of the spreading electrical activity generated by the conditioned stimulus. The structure of the neuron which is mainly affected is the membrane which has a unique natural frequency or set of frequencies. The electrical properties of the membrane depend upon the structure of its protein layers which in turn are a function of the RNA species involved in the synthesis. Thus frequency specific sensitivity of the membrane serves as a mechanism for signal selection.

The two hypotheses are invoked to operate as follows.

> A CS causes a unique pattern of impulses in neurons of the cortical and subcortical projections of the afferents which it excites. Since each of these projection neurons has a unique biochemical "name," each propagates a spreading potential with characteristic ac frequency components. The compound FM signal thus produced is distributed widely in the brain, pratically in the "association" areas of the frontal and temporal poles, following the paths of least electrical resistance, e.g., flowing through the neuroglia. Glial cells throughout the regions reached by these signals are then, somehow, induced to make available RNA types which can produce membranes that respond to the same frequencies. These RNA molecules are presumed to accumulate at the glial-neural junctures during the CS-US interval. A US occurring at this point in time causes a certain number of neurons to fire, and the reversed electrical field of the action potential results in the electrophoretic migration of new RNA into these neurons. This RNA is then assumed to "transform" the protein synthesizing apparatus of the incorporating neurons in such a way that their membranes become sensitive to the FM signals which represent the CS. Thus, on subsequent occurrences of the CS these neurons are more likely to fire (pp. 172-173).

The Landauer hypotheses appear to involve both quantitative changes (induction of glial RNA) and qualitative ones (the incorporation of glial RNA in neural DNA so that new RNA and protein molecules develop). One serious obstacle for this scheme is the recent observation (Bullock, 1964) that there is little current spread between glial cells and neurons in the leech but great current spread between glia. However, the leech system may not be representative of the nervous system of other organisms in this aspect.

Bonner (1964, 1966) suggested that histones repressed the functioning of DNA and that nerve impulses would cause a derepression of gene sites such that increased amounts of RNA would be produced. The gene once derepressed may remain derepressed permanently and provide a means of encoding for permanent memory. He suggested GABA as the derepressing substance which is stored in the dendrites at the synapse and is released during stimulation. GABA is unique to brain tissue and is formed in moth inhibitory and excitatory neurons in the perpheral nervous system. GABA has been indicated to be the only blocking compound out of ten extracted from peripheral nerves of lobsters which is in much higher concentration in efferent inhibitory than in excitatory azons (Bullock, 1964). Studies of the enzymes involved in GABA metabolism in isolated axons show that inhibitory axons form GABA two to six times more rapidly than excitatory axons. Other research which is related to the possible inhibitory functions of GABA is summarized in Chapter 2.

For Bonner the GABA would derepress gene sites so as to synthesize the messenger RNA to make more enzymes for the synthesis of GABA and other substances. Bonner also suggested that GABA could act as a sensitizer of dendrites for synaptic transmission.

Although Dingman and Sporn (1961) had claimed that the primary, secondary or tertiary structure of RNA might be involved directly in learning events, they have since rejected that hypothesis (1964). They suggested that if one is concerned with locating memory traces in the nervous system, no single molecule can be regarded as the sole engram and that lipids should be given consideration for their role (as well as other molecules including RNA and proteins); they also thought that synaptic events were of importance in memory.

In an attempt to integrate neurological and chemical events in the brain, Barondes (1965) postulated that memory storage is based on the development of new synaptic connections with protein molecules being intimately involved in this process. The connections would be formed either by biosynthesis or by molecular rearrangement of a protein. The stimulus for the change could be a neurotransmitter substance or other substances released during neural activation. The change could occur either in the pre- or postsynaptic neuron, or in both. The possible presynaptic mechanisms were outgrowth of axonal substance, increased synthesis of transmitter and altered release of transmitter. The possible postsynaptic mechanisms were outgrowth of dendritic processes, increased synthesis of receptor, increased sensitivity of receptor, increased permeability to transmitter and decreased degradation of transmitter. Although development of the connection could be based on either biosynthesis or molecular rearrangement, Barondes thought that maintenance of the connection involved some type of biosynthetic activity. He also maintained that RNA, lipids, and other substances probably participate in the development and maintenance of synaptic connections.

Other theoretical suggestions have been offered in the interesting book, *Macromolecular Specificity and Biological Memory,* edited by Schmitt (1962).

In general it can be seen that there has been a shift away from the emphasis on the primary structure of nucleic acids to quaternary aspects involving the interaction of two or more types of molecules as in enzyme induction and DNA- histone complexing ideas. Associated with this shift is the increasing concern with multiple macromolecules such as lipids and proteins as suggested by Dingman and Sporn (1964) and by Barondes (1965). However, the suggestion of the former individuals that one can not think of RNA or any single molecule as containing the memory trace because a sequence of events are involved in learning need not deter theorists from considering any single molecule as a memory molecule. Obviously multiple chemical events underlie all behavior and no molecule performs its function in isolation. When McConnell or Hyden or any other individual speaks of RNA as the memory molecule he is suggesting not that RNA is the only molecule which is involved in learning events but that

RNA has the *potential* for precipitating certain chemical functions (within the appropriate chemical environment) which have
been associated with the previous stimulating conditions. This
procedure is similar to that of molecular biologists who speak of
DNA as a "genetic coder" or as containing "genetic memory."
Obviously, DNA contains nothing but a *potential* and it requires
assistance from other chemicals in order for the potential to be
actualized.

An interesting aspect of some theories in this area (Hyden and
Landauer), as well as in neuropsychology (e.g., Galambos, 1961;
Pribram, 1963*b*), is the increased importance attached to glial
cells in complex behavior. Although the suggestions are unique
and of great interest, the evidence cited is of circumstantial
nature. This is true of the Hyden results which show a relationship between glial and neural RNA. To show the causal relationship that he is assuming occurs, he would need, for instance, to
produce changes in glial RNA and note the effect on neural RNA.
A simple procedure might involve injecting tritiated uridine
(which would be incorporated into RNA), sacrificing the animals
at varying time periods afterwards, extracting glial and neural
RNA, and determining the amount of label in each. This procedure could be supplemented with autoradiography and electron
microscopy for corroborative purposes. Presumably, if Hyden's
ideas are correct, one would expect that during learning events
the glial RNA should show labeling, and the labeled material
should gradually shift to neural sites.

CHAPTER 10

CONCLUSIONS AND RESEARCH SUGGESTIONS

T HE NUCLEIC ACID researchers concerned with learning phenomena have been of two general types: those such as the McGill University group (Cameron and Solyom, Kral and Sved) who have been concerned with the applied or therapeutic aspects of RNA, and those interested in the more theoretical problem, that of determining the molecular basis for learning phenomena. However, many of the latter group could be interested in therapeutic applications. It appears that the first experiments of both groups in this area have been of a groping nature with the expectation that decisive answers to the problem could be obtained quickly and easily. However, even though the enthusiasm of researchers is still at a high level, it is now realized by most investigators that the problem must be handled by systematic programs of long duration.

The experiments so far have been mainly concerned with one or the other of the nucleic acids and have been of a one-shot nature (Corning and John, 1961; Dingman and Sporn, 1961; Cook *et al.*, 1963), or if or a systematic nature the work is indirect and inconclusive (Cameron and Solyom, 1961; Zelman, Kabot, Jacobson and McConnell, 1963) or does not include all relevant variables (Hyden, 1961, 1962; Hyden and Egyhazi, 1962, 1963, 1964).

The experimental results tend to suggest that RNA is involved in learning phenomena. However, there is some question as to whether it is performing a general function for cellular metabolism (see Chapter 9) or whether it is specific and unique to the learning events. In this chapter we will be devoted to four functions: (1) to consider basic problems; (2) to evaluate critically the RNA hypothesis; (3) to indicate several related facts which seem clear cut, and (4) to suggest the use of these facts as a means of investigating behvaioral events.

PROBLEMS IN MOLECULAR PSYCHOBIOLOGICAL RESEARCH

The research program suggested below is only one of a number that might be undertaken. It is valuable to face the question of the neurochemical correlates of learning and other behavior with multiple approaches. In so doing there are a number of problems one faces.

General Versus Specific Cellular Functions

One of the problems in investigating biological events at the cellular level is that there is a confounding of general functions of the cell (metabolism) with that of certain specific functions, e.g., memory formation (assuming that there is a cellular basis for this event). (See Chapter 6.) Thus the investigator must use techniques which will allow an estimate of this specific function divorced from the general metabolic events. Unfortunately, most of the procedures employed to date in the investigation of nucleic acids have not been pertinent to the special function alone. One possible way to handle this difficulty is to analyze the nucleic acids from a number of tissues. By noting similarities and differences, one might be able to determine the specific contributions. Furthermore, if adaptive behavior is directly dependent upon nucleic acid function in neural tissue, then one would expect that the nucleic acids of neural and nonneural tissues should be different in some respects. Unfortunately, in most experiments there has been no attention devoted to nucleic acid structure and activity both in neural and nonneural tissue.

There are at least two other important problems: what methods provide the most plausible means for determining the neurochemical process underlying learning, and what animal to use in experimentation.

Methods

A major problem in discovering the neurochemical aspects of the memory process is in determining how to distinguish an "unchanged" from a "changed" molecule or molecular system. There are two broad approaches to this problem, the direct and indirect methods. The direct method provides information specific to the suggested mechanism of change whereas the indirect procedures require more inferences as to the mechanism of change. Unfortunately, at the present time any direct procedures would not be sensitive enough to detect changes and one if forced to use indirect procedures. Some possible methods are treated in Appendix A and will not be repeated here.

Suitable Experimental Animal

Planaria have been popular with some researchers. The advantages of this organism are the cost and ease of maintenance and the possibility of obtaining identical animals by regeneration. However, even though one can obtain biologically inactive DNA and RNA for analytic purposes, biologically active nucleic acids would be difficult, if not impossible, to extract from single planaria. Furthermore, it would be even more difficult to extract nucleic acids from neural tissue or to fractionate the separate RNA species. Thus the planarian offers only limited possibilities for research.

The most effective animal for determining the molecular basis for learning events would appear to be one of the higher animals, e.g., rats, cats, dogs, etc. With these animals one can do an analysis on the nucleic acids with single animals, even obtaining biologically active DNA and RNA in nervous tissue or fractionating the RNA species. It is important to analyze the nucleic acids of single animals in that memory is an individual problem, i.e., if one averages over a number of animals, interesting results can be obscured. This event is one which has been prominently indicated in a number of investigations.

EVALUATION

The results seem to indicate that RNA is involved in some way in learning phenomena. However, it is probable that RNA constituents function as metabolites which affect the overall function of the cell and indirectly affect learning. Ribonucleotides are important as portions of coenzymes and for other cellular activities. Results by Weiss and Sokoloff (1963), relating thyroxine activity and protein synthesis, support the possibility that RNA activity varies directly with cellular metabolism. (See other comments in Chapter 9.)

The main problem faced by advocates of the RNA hypothesis is that RNA is not of a single homogeneous type. There are a number of RNA fractions as indicated above. Which one of these fractions carries the experiential code? Messenger RNA may appear unsuitable because of its short life, functioning on the average only ten to twenty times in bacteria (Watson, 1963). However, there is some information which suggests that messenger RNA in some mammalian tissues has a longer life (e.g., Scott and Bell, 1964; Sonneborn, 1964; Di Girolamo, Henshaw, and Hiatt, 1964). The last group indicated that cytoplasmic messenger RNA is stable for at least twenty hours. This event might suggest the possibility that this RNA species could be important in learning events. Transfer and ribosomal RNA appear unlikely as candidates for the memory process because of their known simple functions. However, either or both of these latter could be involved indirectly in many behavioral events, *e.g.*, increasing amounts of ribosomal RNA might increase the rate and quantity of protein synthesized.

The earlier work evaluating total RNA is of little value relative to the memory hypothesis in that all fractions are confounded; obviously some of the RNA's are not uniquely involved in memory. In recent experiments, Hyden and Egyhazi (1962) have separated nuclear and cytoplasmic RNA. They suggested chromosomal RNA as a molecule involved in memory. However, both nuclear and cytoplasmic RNA each contain at least three fractions and confounding is still present.

Because the idea of base changes in learning events has had such a tremendous effect on those individuals supporting the RNA hypothesis, it is worthwhile to look at various possible interpretations for Hyden's report of base changes in RNA (See Chapter 9). One obvious possibility is a quantitative change, a statistical artifact because of pooling. A number of RNA fractions are confounded in each analysis; therefore, in that the fractions differ in base amounts it is possible that the fractions may be increasing in gross amounts at different rates, giving the appearance of base changes in specific molecules. For example, assume that there are only two fractions confounded and the amount of A is 20 per cent in one and 25 per cent in the other. Assume also that under normal conditions the two fractions are present in equal amounts. The mean amount of A present in the sample would be 22.5 per cent. If under experimental conditions the first increased ten times as fast as the second, the mean amount of A would be 20.5 per cent, suggesting a qualitative change in polymer RNA when only a quantitative event has occurred. In some of Hyden's later research he seems to be implying that this event is occurring.

Another possible interpretation for the base changes is that the polymer RNA population of cells in changing, a qualitative change. Hyden at first spoke of polymer RNA in cells being modified by electrical events; later he suggested a changing cell population because of the entry of RNA nucleotides from surrounding glia.

Of the two possibilities, the first is the most plausible. There is no doubt from molecular biological studies that this event occurs; there is no reason to suspect that during learning, cellular events should be drastically different as would be the case in the second interpretation.

One of the main theses by Hyden in that these changes occur only during learning and then only in neural sites directly involved in the learning event. However, there are data showing that base changes in neural tissue are not unique to learning situations.

1) Egyhazi and Hyden (1961) noted that the administration of malononitrile caused an increase of 25 per cent in the amounts of RNA and proteins in nerve cells and a decrease of 45 per cent in glial RNA. The C in nerve cells decreased by approximately 6 per cent; glial cells showed a 20 per cent increase in this base. The G in glial RNA decreased also by 25 per cent.

2) Geiger (1957) reported that electrical stimulation of the cortex for thirty seconds brought about an increase in the C and A content whereas the amounts of U and G remained constant. He concluded that brain nucleic acids are broken down during increased activity and quickly resynthesized after cessation of the stimulation.

3) Grampp and Edstrom (1963) found that a six hour excita-

tion of crustacean stretch receptors did not affect the RNA content of the receptor cells but the A/U ratio of the RNA increased significantly.

4) Edstrom (1964) showed that no changes in gross amounts of RNA occurred in the axon and myelin sheath of the Mauthner nerve fiber of the goldfish following spinal cord transection whereas marked changes resulted in the A/G ratio; the greatest value occurred two to three days after transection. Previous investigators (e.g., Hyden) had not found RNA in the axon of other animals.

A further major difficulty of the RNA hypothesis is that the RNA molecules appear to be too labile to subserve a memory function which demands a moderate degree of stability. During activity gross changes in RNA amounts occur which are usually of a transient nature. For example, Geiger *et al.* (1956) stimulated the brain cortex of cats and found a change in nucleic acids in the stimulated areas, which was reversible in minutes. Others have reported similar results (Hyden, 1961). However, Hyden and Egyhazi (1962) claimed that preliminary data indicated that changes in base amounts persisted in nuclear RNA for forty-eight hours. Yet in other work (1963) they found no base changes in nuclear RNA twenty-four hours after stopping the experiment.

Furthermore, in dealing with higher organisms it seems an accepted conclusion that memory functions are subserved by neural tissue, especially cortical or near-cortical neural tissue. Yet most investigators have not employed nonneural tissue as a control to clearly indicate that neural RNA activity is different than that in nonneural tissue. The changes reported by Hyden and others may be no different than are the changes in nonneural tissue. RNA changes should occur in any *functionally active cell,* neural or nonneural, during protein synthesis.

Another consideration, suggested by Dingman and Sporn (1963), is related to the RNA injection experiments. Even if experimental results were consistently positive showing that RNA could pass specific information from one organism to another, this result does not indicate that RNA is the basic memory molecule. For example, DNA contains the necessary information for protein synthesis; however, protein synthesis can not be effected by DNA. The information must be transcribed in an intermediary molecule, messenger RNA, before the message can be translated or actualized in protein synthesis. The same set of events might be involved in memory with DNA being the basic molecule but requiring the mediation of an RNA for the memory to be transmitted. Thus, RNA would be a necessary molecule but not a sufficient one. It is probable that both DNA and RNA will be found to be necessary molecules, but neither alone would be sufficient to handle learning phenomena.

Finally, RNA is an intermediary between DNA and protein in genetic information transfer and it seems unlikely that such an "errand boy" is going to be of greater importance for experiential information.

In spite of the above consideration, individuals tend to accept the RNA hypothesis. Therefore, let us look at the main research results which purport to suggest this hypothesis. A careful look will show that the results are not unequivocal in nature.

Holger Hyden has influenced the thinking of most individuals who favor the RNA hypothesis. His work has been evaluated above; however, several other points could be made at this time.

Hyden, in his early theory, reported that changes occur in the base ratios of RNA of nerve cells during learning events. However, as suggested above, these base changes in the nerve cells may merely be metabolic events underlying protein synthesis during activity. The changes in neural RNA may be no different than that in the RNA of nonneural cells during activity, e.g., muscle cells. Hyden has not included analyses on nonneural cells as a control. Information from such analyses would be valuable.

Furthermore, sensory stimulation is required for learning and memory to occur. But all sensory stimulation does not result in the development of memory traces. Thus his experimental results may not be related to learning and memory. Many individuals would question whether the experiments he describes as learning would be clear cut examples of this process (Hyden and Egyhazi, 1962, 1963, 1964). Does the rat moving up the wire to the platform where food is located, or being forced to use the left hand rather than the right, constitute learning as it is usually defined? The first event, balancing on the wire, would seem more likely to be construed as learning than would the second. It might be considered similar to the learning of a skill.

Hyden usually analyzes the RNA base changes of neural cells in the medulla. Most of his analyses have been on the large Deiter cells of the vestibular nucleus in the medulla, cells which are active during stimulation of the vestibular mechanism in the inner ear. Even in some of the simple "learning" experiments he analyzed the Deiter cells. Yet there is no indication that the vestibular nucleus is involved in any events beyond sensory stimulation. An important addition to his experimentation would be analyses on cells at higher brain levels, especially in the cerebral cortex, which are intimately involved in learning. Only the experiment on change of handedness in rats involved an analysis of cortical cells, in the motor area. Further cortical analyses are required.

Thus the conclusion which follows from a careful analysis of the Hyden experiments is that RNA changes occur when cells are active. Nothing definite about memory functions has been clearly indicated.

Another research which people believe support the RNA hypothesis is that by Corning and John (1961). These individuals conditioned planaria, transected them and allowed some to regenerate in RNase and others in pond water. They believed that the RNase should "erase" the memories in altered RNA as the RNA was passed to the regenerating tissue. They reported that heads which had regenerated in RNase displayed a retention level equal to that of head and tail sections which had regenerated in pond water; however, tails regenerated in RNase performed randomly. They maintained that these results were consistent with the RNA hypothesis if one allows for the fact that the head is the dominant region of the planarian.

A number of possible questions might be raised relative to this experiment. It appears that the most serious point is whether RNase had any effect during regeneration. Corning and John did not control the medium and check after the RNase treatment to determine if any breakdown products were present. Furthermore, RNase will degrade RNA only if it is isolated. Regenerating tissue is covered with a membrane and the RNA would not be readily accessible to the RNase, even though small smounts of the dilute solution might penetrate the membrane.

If one allows that the RNase would have access to the RNA, another serious question arises. If the RNase degraded the RNA, why would it select only the "altered RNA," the memory RNA. It should degrade any and all RNA in the regenerating portion; one would expect that the RNA of the regenerating end would be broken down continuously such that regeneration could not occur because no protein would be available.

Hyden and his colleagues and Corning and John have been careful in specifying that the results only suggest that *RNA may be the memory molecule.* (e.g., John, 1964). However, in the enthusiasm for work in this area some individuals tend to overlook the word "may."

The important point of the above discussion is that *there is no crucial experiment which has unequivocally implicated RNA uniquely in memory functions.* However, in all fairness to advocates of the RNA hypothesis, it is entirely possible that future research will show conclusively that they are correct in their hypothesis.

The RNA injection experiment offers an interesting experimental tool. However, the results indicating that animals injected with "sophisticated" RNA are superior to those injected with "naive" RNA are inconclusive and leave much to be desired. Six interrelated questions immediately are raised.

Does the RNA have an effect?

If an effect occurs, is it due to the intact molecule, or to breakdown products, reaching the brain?

Is the effect a general one or is it specific?

If only breakdown products reach the brain, are they utilized in the synthesis of new RNA molecules or in other cellular constituents?

Where in the cell do the RNA constituents go?

Where in the brain do these chemicals go?

There appears to be no conclusive evidence for any of these questions. Radiographic procedures would be valuable tools in attempting answers to the questions. As a beginning experiment the following design might be employed.

1) Four groups of littermate rats would be employed. Each animal would be injected with tritiated uridine prior to the task of concern. One group of animals would be involved in a learning task. A second group would be aurally stimulated for the same period. The third group would receive motor activity. The fourth group of rats would be inactive and serve as a control.

2) Immediately after completion of the task of concern, each animal would be sacrificed, whole brain dissected, and RNA extracted by repeated phenol procedures.

3) Equal *amounts* of RNA from each of these four animals would be injected into four other naive littermates. A fifth littermate would be injected with physiological saline.

4) These five groups of animals would be subjected to the same learning task used in (1) and their behavior noted within a given time period.

5) Immediately after this session each animal would be sacrificed and the cortex and subcortical brain portions sectioned into a number of parts.

6) The RNA constituents in the cell pool (first acid soluble fraction) and the RNA fraction would be extracted by a modification of the Santen-Agranoff procedure (1963) and the amounts determined by the orcinal test. (See Appendix B.)

7) The incorporation of tritiated uridine in these two fractions for the various brain parts and for the five groups would be determined with a liquid scintillation spectrometer. (See Appendix A.)

8) With some of the animals in the five groups, autoradiographs would be prepared and utilized with light and electron microscopes to determine where in the cell the tritium is located.

The behavioral comparisons between the five groups, as well as the biochemical and radiographic comparisons between brain parts and cell portions, would provide some preliminary answers to the above questions. Obviously, a number of experiments would be required to obtain definitive answers.

ACCEPTABLE FACTS

Even though the research relative to the nucleic acids and memory is inconclusive, two related facts seem clear cut: the amount of RNA per cell gradually increases to a maximum over long periods of time and superimposed on this long term are transient changes in RNA content of cells. The reports by Hyden, Leslie and others in Chapters 8 and 9 support this statement. The rapid increases of RNA following hormonal injections, enzyme induction and other phenomena discussed in Chapter 6 are pertinent also. These results are probably indicating that during activity of cells and tissue, DNA is performing a basic function in the synthesis of RNA. Attending the RNA changes are the reported increments in the content of proteins and lipids which would be required in growth and the elaboration of the cell membrane and synaptic extension.

Thus from the above results one could be tempted to hypothesize that learning is no different than other regulation events such as cell differentiation except in the mechanism by which the function of DNA is brought about. However, the scientific techniques to determine directly these mechanisms are not available at this time. Thus one must take an indirect approach.

RESEARCH PROGRAM

One possible research program suitable to present techniques would involve three stages: (1) to determine the brain loci showing rapid RNA synthesis during learning events; (2) to determine if the RNA synthesized is necessary or incidental for learning purposes, and (3) to determine if the RNA synthesized is a new species or is more of the RNA which is available during usual conditions.

Brain Loci?

One indirect approach is suggested by the fact that Izawa, Allfrey and Mirsky (1963), Beermann and Clever (1964), and Edstrom (1964) showed that the RNA/DNA ratio for active DNA sites is much greater than for nonactive sites. Therefore, if one were to expose one animal to an involved learning task and sacrifice him while he is learning, the amount of RNA synthesized by a given amount of DNA (RNA/DNA ratio) should be greater than that of a littermate restricted during the same time period to no, or a lesser degree of, learning. This result would not provide definite information concerning memory mechanisms but would provide an indirect procedure relating behavioral events to patterns of RNA synthesis in the brain. Thus the RNA/DNA ratio would provide an index to chemical and brain functioning.

The author has obtained preliminary results which suggest the usefulness of the RNA/DNA ratio as a suitable indicator. Short-term memory underlying learning of an association between bar pressing and the obtaining of food was of concern. Four pairs of littermate rats were the subjects (two pairs — Sprague-Dawley; two pairs — Hooded). Each pair of animals was moved from the main animal quarters to a separate room eight to ten days before actual use and placed on a forty-six-hour deprivation schedule. Each pair received familiarization training with an operant conditioning box; each learned to press the bar and to eat from the food cup. When ready for the learning event one of the two animals was randomly chosen and placed in the operant conditioning box (experimental). The other animal (control) remained in the home cage. The experimental animal spent ten to twenty-two minutes learning that pressing the bar would deliver food. Three of the experimental animals of the four pairs showed definite learning within fifteen minutes as indicated both by objective recording of responses and by observation by several experimenters; the fourth animal required twenty-two minutes. While learning, the animal was sacrificed by decapitation and liver, kidney and brain portions were removed. The brain was sectioned into ten parts — anterior, medial and posterior portions of the dorsal cortex, the same portions of the ventral cortex, cerebral hemispheres less the cortex, cerebellum, upper brain stem (sectioned below the inferior colleculi) and lower brain stem. The separation of dorsal and ventral cortex was at the rhinal fissure. Control animals were sacrificed in a similar fashion and the same tissue removed.

DNA and RNA were extracted from each tissue with a modified Schmidt-Thannheuser procedure (Santen and Agranoff, 1963). (See Appendix B). Orcinol and diphenylamine tests indicated the amounts of RNA and DNA, respectively. The RNA/DNA ratios of control and experimental animals for each tissue were compared.

In this experiment a confounding of learning with sensory stimulation and motor activity was involved; however, the main purpose of this study was whether the RNA/DNA ratio would be able to discriminate between groups of animals in grossly different conditions. The results with four replications are shown in Table 10-I. The anterior portion of the dorsal cortex (according to electrophysiological criteria, the motor area) showed a greater RNA/DNA ratio in experimental than in control animals. This appeared to be indicating the effects of motor activity for when the size of the operant conditioning apparatus was decreased during the last two replications (reducing the available space in which to locomote), the difference disappeared. The difference was great in the first two replications such that an overall difference was still suggested by the data. The posterior portion of the ventral cortex showed a greater ratio for the experimental animals. This portion is in the entorhinal area and probably includes a portion of the hippocampus. It is interesting that the results of Flexner, Flexner and Stellar (1963) with puromycin in-

TABLE 10-I
MEANS AND STANDARD DEVIATIONS FOR MEAN RNA/DNA
RATIOS OF NEURAL AND NONNEURAL TISSUES IN
CONTROL AND EXPERIMENTAL ANIMALS

| | | *Tissues* | | | | | |
		AD	MD	PD	AV	MV	PV
Exp.	M	2.69	0.82	0.97	0.69	0.93	1.56
	SD	3.70	1.00	0.65	0.33	0.17	1.08
Cont.	M	1.08	0.89	0.78	0.62	1.17	0.60
	SD	1.20	0.50	0.41	0.25	0.61	0.15
		CH	CB	UBS	LBS	L	K
Exp.	M	0.72	0.23	0.88	0.88	1.26	0.42
	SD	0.25	0.02	0.58	0.37	0.62	0.10
Cont.	M	0.72	0.23	0.59	1.04	1.50	0.42
	SD	0.40	0.08	0.23	0.80	1.17	0.05

jections suggested the involvement of this tissue in memory. These results are also consistent with those of Adey and others discussed in Chapter 2 and with the notion that the posterior cortex is involved in discrimination learning (Galambos and Morgan, 1960; Pribram, 1960). The other tissues appear not to contribute in the learning task, including the liver and kidney as one would expect.

In view of these results and those discussed in Chapter 2 concerning the importance of the hippocampus, it is worthwhile to note that there are indications that protein metabolism in the hippocampus is greater than in the dorsal cortex (MacLean, 1960). Likewise, the serotonin content (considered by some to be a transmitter substance) is greater in the hippocampus and the tranquilizing drug reserpine (which is supposed to release bound serotonin) elicits distinctive EEG changes in the hippocampus.

One problem with the above approach is that the increase in RNA during various behavioural events may be so small compared to the amount of RNA normally in the cell that the RNA/DNA ratio will not be discriminative, i.e., the "noise" level will be too great. Thus to improve the present approach extraction only of nuclear DNA and RNA could be attempted. This procedure will eliminate the cytoplasmic RNA which constitutes most of the RNA in the cell and allow the detection of RNA increases as they are occuring. Another possibility would be to utilize the protein/DNA ratio as an index because it appears to be more sensitive. The amount of protein per cell may be one-hundred times as great as the amount of RNA.

These results tend to suggest the potential usefulness of these ratios as indices of functional activity. Obviously, further evaluation with learning and other behavioral events in well-controlled experiments is required. If the results of further work are consistent with the present results, these ratios could provide powerful means for mapping brain function and assessing biochemical events during transient and long term sensory stimulation (or lack of stimulation), during motor activity, during various types of learning, in emotional phenomena such as stress, and in other behavioral events.

The experiment with radioactive RNA injections discussed under "Evaluation" would also provide useful information concerning brain loci functional during learning.

Is RNA Necessary?

Once that information has been obtained concerning the critical loci involved in learning and other behavior, experiments could be instituted to determine if RNA synthesis is necessary or incidental for learning events. For example, in an experiment concerned with learning, two groups of rats would be used. One group would have injections of actinomycin D (which inhibits RNA synthesis by binding G sites on DNA). The animals would be subjected to a learning task several hours later and their learning ability determined. The other group of animals would have injections of physiological saline solutions and then given the same learning task. (One or more other control groups might be employed; however, our interest in this discussion is only on the two groups.) All animals would be sacrificed and DNA and RNA extracted. The actinomycin animals should have reduced amounts of RNA in the critical loci. If they also showed impaired learning ability, this result would suggest that RNA synthesis is necessary for learning. If reduced RNA occurred but learning ability was unimpaired, this result would suggest that RNA synthesis is incidental. Further experiments with various learning tasks would be conducted to provide definitive results.

This stage of experimentation, although logically following the first stage, might be discarded because of the difficulty in obtaining definitive results due to the toxic effects of the antibiotic. Animals given actinomycin D will eventually die and one must conduct the experiments before definite gross behavioral abnormalities occur. Barondes and Jarvik (1964) reported that actinomycin D had no effect on animals in a passive avoidance learning situation even though the dosage of actinomycin D produced 83 per cent inhibition of brain RNA synthesis in mice. One factor that introduces difficulty in interpreting these results is that the degree of inhibition was determined in animals not subjected to the learning task. It is possible that the mild shock used to produce avoidance responses could have affected the actinomycin binding such that inhibition in the learning animals might have been less than the 83 per cent reported. In this connection, it has been indicated that malononitrile will prevent this antibiotic from inhibiting RNA synthesis.

Appel (1964) has found that in some tasks learning is impaired by actinomycin D whereas it is not affected in others. In a novelty test and in learning to escape from a maze by swimming (and retention of this habit), actinomycin had no effect. The antibiotic did have a negative effect for mice in learning to jump to a ledge from an electrified grid and on a conditioned pole-avoidance response. In the last case injected mice showed impairment of retention for avoidance behavior but escape behavior was not affected.

An approach that is somewhat related is the one by the University of Pennsylvania group (Flexner, Flexner and Stellar) who are asking the question, "Is protein necessary for memory?" They use puromycin, an antibiotic which inhibits protein synthesis but whose effects are reversible, i.e., are not lethal when given in suitable dosage. They have found (1963) that injections bilaterally in the posterior temporal lobe area twenty-four hours after learning will eradicate memory for a learned avoidance response. They report that it is necessary to obtain 80 per cent or greater inhibition of protein synthesis lasting from eight to ten hours for memory to be affected. To eliminate memory after much longer periods of time, e.g., twelve days, puromycin must be injected into larger portions of the brain.

Unique Species?

Experiments could be conducted to determine if the RNA synthesized in critical loci during learning was a new or unique species or was merely increased amounts of the usual RNA involved in protein synthesis (messenger, transfer and ribosomal). DNA-RNA hybridization experiments (Bonner, 1964) provide a possible means to handle this problem.

One simple experiment would be the following. Two groups of rats would be employed. One group would be exposed to learning tasks and sacrificed. The other group would not be trained prior to sacrificing. Liver, brain tissue critical for learning, and brain tissue not critical for learning would be extracted. Biologically active RNA would be obtained from all tissues and biologically active DNA would be extracted from the liver by repeated phenol treatments. The liver DNA of both groups of animals would be denatured with sodium hydroxide, and single strand DNA trapped on nitrocellulose membranes. Then increasing amounts of RNA would be added to allow DNA-RNA hybridizing to occur. RNase would then be introduced in the solution to eliminate noncomplementary (nonhomologous) pairing and to determine the maximum amount of RNA which would hybridize with a given amount of RNA.

Radioactive labeling of RNA and spectrophotometric analyses would provide information concerning the degree of RNA hybridizing with DNA. The RNA from liver, RNA from critical brain loci and RNA from noncritical loci would be hybridized separately with liver RNA for both learning and non-learning animals. If a new species of RNA occurs through modification of basic RNA during learning, as some RNA proponents claim, or if a unique RNA is synthesized during learning, the degree of hybridization with the RNA from critical loci should not be the same in both learning and non-learning animals. If the degree of hybridization is the same in all three cases for learning and non-learning animals, the hypothesis of a new species of RNA would seem doubtful. A further interesting step would be to add RNA from critical loci of the learning animal to the hybrid of liver DNA and RNA from critical loci of the non-learning animal. Likewise, RNA from critical loci of the non-learning animal could be added to the hybrid of the learning animal. If a unique species of RNA were involved, increased hybridization would occur in the first case but not in the second. A number of similar experiments would be required to obtain definitive results.

If the results suggested a new species of RNA, experiments to determine the characteristics of this RNA would be undertaken. If a new species were not indicated, interest would be directed to DNA and DNA-complexing to determine the mechanisms responsible for increased RNA synthesis.

These same three stages could be employed also with other

than learning events, e.g., during sensory stimulation, motor activity, etc. Furthermore, the same multistage program could concentrate on the uniqueness of protein for behavioral events by a few modifications to the procedures.

CHAPTER 11

THEORETICAL SPECULATIONS

Having looked at data and ideas of molecular biology, neurobiology, and molecular psychobiology, it would seem appropriate to integrate the material into a model of behavior utilizing a set of tentative hypotheses. Obviously such a model would involve much speculation and contain many gaps; however, it could serve as a framework for future research. We will proceed by setting up hypotheses which will be discussed in some detail.

GENERAL

1) *Contained within the genes (i.e., the DNA molecules) is the potential of the organism. This potential represents a range of possibilities for the organism relative to physical and behavioral functioning.*

2) *The DNA passes the genetic code to the RNA molecule. Thus the RNA receives the basic instructions in the linear sequence code from DNA.*

This process is called transcription. The information encoded in RNA is then translated into the synthesis of specific proteins. (1) and (2) are well accepted by scientists and have been discussed above.

3) *Most of the DNA complexes are in inactive form until appropriately stimulated. Upon adequate stimulation the DNA is activated and rapidly synthesizes RNA so that protein synthesis can occur.*

The work on enzyme induction, hormonal activation, loss of histones and stimulation and learning events discussed in earlier chapters suggests this possibility. Some of the DNA sites must be active from conception in that the mitotic process is carried on with cell division occurring. But most DNA sites must be silent. Whether the DNA is repressed by histones, repressors synthesized by regulator genes or other molecules, or is merely in dormant state is not certain. What is certain, however, is that DNA is activated to perform its basic function of synthesizing RNA. For purposes of convenience we will assume that an active inhibition or repression is effected by the complexing of histones with DNA so that the RNA polymerase is unable to effect RNA synthesis by DNA.

Presumably the stimulation would result in a temporary change in the histones of particular segments of the DNA complex. Possibly the histones change in configuration or loosen their binding with DNA so that the RNA polymerase can activate DNA sites. Or the reversible type of change suggested by Allfrey, Faulkner and Mirsky (1964) might turn on and off RNA synthesis. (See Chapter 9.) This modification of DNA complexes would probably require special chemical conditions within the nerve cell and would be effected only within narrow limits. For example, narrow margins of pH or ionic concentrations might be required. Thus this modification would result in a development of the potential. The experimental stimulation or experiential coding would merely be the genetic code in operation. The stimulation could be initiated from outside the organism or be changes in the internal state of the organism.

4) *Each segment of most DNA molecules (a cistron) is specialized to produce different phenotypic or behavioral effects as a result of RNA and protein synthesis.*

This is widely accepted by molecular biologists. Even though each cell nucleus contains the same potential information in its DNA as do other cells all of this information is not being expressed in every cell. The chromosomal puffs showing DNA activation in insects are the best evidence to illustrate this aspect. It has been observed that different gene sites puff in different tissues and that different sites puff in the same tissue at different times; hormonal eliciting of puffs at specific chromosomal sites is followed by developmental changes. The different cistrons code for unique RNA and protein molecules in many cases. However, some cistrons may produce the same RNA and protein molecules as others; the phenotypic differences might be produced by differential degrees of susceptibility of DNA to activation.

5) *Within the chromosomes only a certain number of genes*

are concerned with the basic potential for visual functions; others operate for auditory tasks; still others, in tactual performance; etc. Thus within each of the areas of the brain which subserve sensory functions will be DNA complexes in which the basic code can be transmitted by the appropriate DNA molecules. The same would be true for genes for motor behavior. These DNA complexes will be receptive to modification by appropriate sensory and motor stimulation, i.e., the histone inhibition decreased so that DNA can be activated. Thus learning involving visual aspects would be indicated by transient changes in occipital lobe complex; auditory experiences would be subserved by temporal lobe molecules; etc. These would be specific contributions. If learning involves visual, auditory and other sensory events, transient modification of DNA complexes would result in a number of portions of the brain so that protein synthesis could be effected. In such cases if damage occurs so as to obliterate several of these, the memory for the event could be maintained by undamaged areas. Complementing the specific contributors in the sensory and motor brain portions would be a general contribution to learning and other events by the upper brain stem reticular system.

Different portions of the brain appear to contribute different functions (Gardner, 1963). (See Chapter 2.) Sensory-motor functions are more easily localizable than are other functions. For example, tissue in the striate area of the occipital lobe in humans is important for visual events and especially for pattern vision. Audition appears to be subserved by tissue in the superior temporal lobe. Likewise, other tissues function for other primary sensory events. The same is true for motor behavior. Motor functions appears to require contributions mainly by tissue in the frontal lobes.

When one considers the localization of more complex functions, problems ensue. A major problem is that the same identical lesion in two individuals produces different symptoms. Only some of these symptoms are related directly to the physical damage; the reactions of the individual to his condition can constitute a major portion of the symptomatology (Goldstein, 1948). Thus, in determining which symptoms directly result from the lesions, the researcher must exclude the psychological symptoms. Then he must infer from the remaining symptoms what functions are subserved by the brain tissue.

In spite of this problem, some progress had been made. The most extreme type of localization of function approach is that of Nielsen (1946). He has different centers for man in cortical tissue for complex functions such as orderly behavior, writing, music making, musical recognition, language formulation, etc. Most individuals are reluctant to localize functions as finely as does Nielsen. For example, Pribram (1960) suggested that tissue in the posterior part of the brain (outside of the primary sensory areas) functions in discriminative behavior whereas the frontal areas are important for intentional or sequential behavior, in conjunction with the limbic regions.

Wooldridge (1963) summarized research by Sperry and by Bures which indicated that the memory trace for learned behavior is stored in the part of the brain that is employed in the sensory recognition or motor control involved directly in the performance of the learned act. For example, Sperry was able to separate one cerebral hemisphere from the other in cats by cutting the interhemispheric connections, the corpus callosum and several other sets of fibers. These split brain cats were taught a pedal pushing tactile discrimination with the left front paw. Then all cortex in the right hemisphere except the sensory and motor areas was removed. The remaining cortex was found to be capable of controlling excellent performance of the learned act; the animals were able also to learn new tactile discriminations with the same left paw. Further similar experiments led Sperry to conclude that he had cornered the memory trace for tactile discrimination in the sensorimotor cortex of the corresponding cerebral hemispheres.

Bures used a reversible decortication procedure. Potassium chloride applied directly to the cortex will inactivate that cortex for various behaviors for a period of several hours. For example, if potassium chloride is applied to both cortices the animal will be incapable of learning even simple tasks. If placed on only one cortex, however, he will function normally. Bures found that a small spot on the cortex could be protected from deactivation by applying a magnesium chloride solution to that spot. Thereby he was able to preserve an island of active tissue in a deactivated zone. This permitted him to do the following experiment. He deactivated one cortex and trained a rat to perform a new routine, thus making use of the other cortex. After waiting a day or two for complete recovery, he deactivated the previously trained cortex except for a selected spot protected by magnesium chloride, and tested the animal's ability to perform the previously learned act. His results were consistent with those by Sperry. If the trained behavior was of a manipulatory nature involving the use of the right paw, protection of the sensorimotor cortex of the left hemisphere preserved the animal's memory of the event for he was able to perform the learned procedure. On the other hand, if the act the rat had been taught involved visual pattern discrimination, protecting only the sensorimotor cortex was ineffective; the visual areas had to be protected against deactivation for the animal to perform the learned response.

In each of the specialized areas the tissue would consist of DNA molecules which provide the basic code for RNA and protein synthesis to maintain the particular function subserved. This code would be transmitted to RNA when the DNA complex was modified during environmental stimulation relating to the particular function during which the molecule is active. The RNA's and proteins provided by different cistrons could be different in some cases and the same in other cases. For example, the DNA or DNA's for visual function would be instrumental in producing RNA_v and $Protein_v$; the DNA for auditory functions would provide RNA_a and $Protein_a$; etc. RNA_v and $Protein_v$ might be different than RNA_a and $Protein_a$. On the other hand, they might be the same. The different effects would be expressed in differential susceptibility of DNA to be activated by the appropriate electrochemical events. If we assume that the RNA's, and likewise proteins, depending on different cistrons are similar, then the phenotypic effects would be due to the availability of varying amounts of RNA and proteins, and other neurochemicals which are involved in the sequence leading to behavior.

Most learning events involve a number of sense modalities. Thus according to the above hypothesis, there would be multiple representation of these events. This possibility fits in well with experiments which show that some memories are relatively unimpaired even with extensive lesions of the brain (Lashley, 1929).

The general contribution to each learning event would be subserved by tissue in the upper brain stem reticular system. This system would have intimate connections with each of the specific contributors during learning events.

Brain stem contribution to learning events has been suggested by experiments of Sperry (cited by Wooldridge, 1963). Split brain monkeys were required to pull the rougher of two levers when one visual pattern appeared and the smoother when another pattern was present. The monkeys were forced to pull the lever, not with the arm controlled by the hemisphere receiving the visual input, but with the other arm which was controlled by the hemisphere that was separated by section of the corpus callosum from all visual input. The animals were able to learn and perform the coordinated event. Thus the tactile and visual contributors were integrated by a subcortical mechanism, presumably the brain stem.

DEVELOPMENT OF SHORT AND LONG TERM MEMORY

6) *As a result of DNA cistrons which are common to a species, neural units are linked together during development.*

There is much evidence indicating that some neural units develop in a relatively fixed pattern during normal development within a species. Obviously, a specific internal chemical environment would be required. Extensive studies by Sperry (1959) involving the switching of muscles or the crossing of nerves led him to conclude that the neural connections necessary for coordinated behavior arise in embryonic development according to a biochemically determined plan which precisely connects the various nerve endings in the body to their corresponding points in the nerve centers of the brain and spinal cord. He indicated that the lower centers in the brain stem and spinal cord were implastic because their function was dictated by their structure, but that higher centers in the brain were capable of modification during extensive learning.

This fixed pattern development should be an expression of definite DNA cistrons being activated at different periods during development.

7) *Stimulation causes nerve impulses in neural units as a result of ACh release, or the release of other transmitters, into synaptic regions.*

This hypothesis is well accepted in neurobiology. Electron microscopy and chemical studies have indicated that packets of ACh exist in presynaptic vesicles. These packets are assumed to be discharged into the synaptic region and to affect graded potentials in the postsynaptic neuron such that a nerve impulse is propagated in that cell. ACh is probably not the only transmitter substance operating at synaptic sites for excitation or inhibition and regulation purposes.

8) *Stimulation results in reverberation in neural circuits. Short term memory can be initiated by the operation of these reverberatory circuits. During reverberation various DNA complexes in neural tissue of certain portions of the brain are stimulated. Short term memory is maintained further by neurochemical events precipitated by reverberation and DNA stimulation.*

Reverberatory circuits have been defined usually to include neurons which are contiguous in a neural net so that nerve impulses can circulate via the synaptic junctions. The definition should also include nonsynaptic communication possibilities, e.g., electrical potentials of neurons in one portion of the brain may excite other neurons at a distance such that the potential of the latter is affected, which in turn feeds back to affect the first group of neurons. Such continued "tuning" could be considered a reverberatory circuit and will be so considered here. Obviously, both the synaptic and nonsynaptic reverberation could coexist. Probably both have importance in brain function; such assumption will be accepted within this theoretical scheme.

The reverberatory circuit model of short term memory is adopted even though some experimental data shows that electrical patterns during learning events are short lived (Morrell, 1961; John, 1961) and data is not always consistent with this idea. However, it is probable that a sequence of chemical events is precipitated by the short-lived reverberation; short-term memory would be maintained by these chemical events until some more durable change occurred. Possibly the graded potentials and the electrical activity of glia participate in the maintenance of these electrical activities.

Suggestions that reverberatory circuits subserve short term memory while some growth is required for relatively permanent memory have been offered by a number of people (e.g., Hebb, 1949; Jeffress, 1951) and there is some experimental data which is consistent with the idea (see Chapter 3). We are merely indicating DNA complexes as the site of influence of the nerve impulses or graded potentials. The DNA complex would be affected by the electrical aspects resulting in a modification of histones with RNA and protein synthesis, and other chemical events, resulting. The exact manner in which the nerve impulses would trigger RNA synthesis is conjectural. It is possible that Hyden's suggestion that a specific frequency of excitation would affect a specific genetic site is appropriate. Or Landauer's conjecture that a spreading electrical potential, rather than the nerve impulse, is the important electrical event, could be invoked.

Alternatively, it is possible that during stimulation there is released at the synapse a chemical (such as GABA as Bonner suggested) which then permeates the soma of the nerve cell and activates DNA in the nucleus. Thus either electrical or chemical agents, or both, would activate DNA sites.

The function of the reverberatory circuit would be to provide for activation of DNA sites so that protein synthesis and other chemical reactions can be effected. The reverberation would allow for continued activation of DNA to occur as long as the reverberation would continue.

Within the reverberatory activity the ACh-AChE activity which the California group have related to adaptive behavior could play an important part as indicated in Hypothesis 7. Variations of these chemicals would provide conditions at the synapse suitable for the transmission of the neural impulse at these functional neural gaps. Thus these activities would be important in maintaining reverberatory circuits of synaptic nature and function as agents for short term memory. These chemicals would facilitate activation of DNA complexes. ACh-AChE activity would be considered *necessary, but not sufficient,* conditions for the development of long term memory. The RNA and protein syntheses would be secondary to the electrochemical events which precede them (Pevzner, 1966), but in the initial development of ACh, AChE, and growth of synaptic and nonsynaptic structure they would be primary.

9) *Some neural activity is present in brain tissue at all times. Even in a relaxed resting state a certain amount of excitation is present. This can be considered to be the background activity. When stimulation is imposed from the exterior, or internally, this background activity is modified. The normal background activity maintains and preserves the DNA complex. The stimulation upsets the equilibrium and allows changes to occur in the complex.*

It appears that the background activity must be of a certain nature for later stimulation to affect the organism. The electroencephalogram (EEG) indicates this activity as varying in amplitude and frequency. It has been demonstrated that when the predominant frequency of the spontaneous electrical activity of the brain (i.e., while at rest) varies greatly from an intermediate range (alphs waves — between 8 and 13 cps — or a little higher) either of a lower or higher frequency, behavior decreases in efficiency (Gaito, 1958; Lindsley, 1960). Thus the spontaneous electrical activity can serve as an index of potential efficiency of behavior; it may also be an index of susceptibility of DNA complex to modification. Usually if the frequency of the spontaneous activity of the brain is in the delta range ($\frac{1}{2}$ to 4 cps), behavior deteriorates (Gaito, 1958; Lindsley, 1960; Simon, 1961). For example, if an individual is given certain commands while his EEG record shows much delta activity, he will be unable to respond and will appear oblivious to his environment (Schwab, 1951). Likewise, the DNA complex would not be receptive to activation during this period. The same reduced ability to learn (i.e., to form some "trace" of an experience) is indicated in dream activity wherein the EEG frequency is below the subjects usual alpha range (Gaito, 1958; Kleitman, 1960) . The dreaming EEG is one or two cps less than his waking frequency. Thus during the dream period the susceptibility to change would be impaired unless the individual is awakened.

Furthermore, Fuster (1958) and Lindsley (1960) have shown that the level of activity of the reticular formation affects perceptual performance. Fuster found that perceptual discrimination was more effective and reaction time decreased when a certain intensity of stimulation of the reticular formation was imposed. Lindsley reported that reticular stimulation increased the visual resolvability capabilities of cats. Two flashes of light separated by 50 milliseconds brought only one evoked potential; however, with five seconds of reticular stimulation the cortex showed two evoked potentials. These data could indicate that reticular activity is modifying the background activity of critical brain sites and is facilitating the activation of DNA sites to allow more efficient operation of the nucleic acid code for the sensory function.

Lindsley (1958) has introduced an interesting notion in his concept of cortical excitability cycles or alpha excitability cycles. These cycles represent a mechanism by means of which the cortex protects itself from constant bombardment through all sensory channels. For example, if a network of neurons were dominated by a ten-per-second beat, only ten times per second could sensory messages be effective. This would involve a waxing and waning or gating mechanism. A reaction time experiment was conducted in which brain waves of the subjects were recorded. The briefest reaction times occurred during a specific portion of the alpha wave; this result was assumed to be evidence favoring the excitability cycle hypothesis.

10) *During DNA activation at least four types of RNA would be synthesized: ribosomal RNA, messenger RNA for ribosomal proteins, messenger RNA for synaptic and nonsynaptic proteins and messenger RNA for enzymes and proteins involved in lipid synthesis and lipid transport.*

This hypothesis attempts to handle the long term increases in ribosomes and ribosomal RNA and the short term increases in RNA, protein, and lipid discussed in Chapter 8. Obviously, other RNA's might be synthesized.

The first messenger RNA would be responsible for the synthesis of ribosomal protein which together with the ribosomal RNA would be incorporated into ribosomes. Ribosomal RNA is as stable as DNA and thus greater numbers of ribosomes would be available after stimulation than before. Because this RNA is stable, very small amounts could accumulate over time as was suggested by Kjelgaard and Kurland (1963) who reported that ribosomal RNA was related to growth in bacteria. Thus with a small increase in ribosomal RNA and ribosomal protein, more ribosomes would be available to increase future synthesis of proteins. The increase might be so small with single periods of stimulation as to be undetectable. But if stimulation of a varied nature were continued intermittently over long periods of time as is the case in the procedures of Krech, Rosenzweig and Bennett, increased numbers of ribosomes should be ascertained. As indicated above ribosomes appear to be the vehicles on which protein synthesis occurs. Thus one effect of stimulation would be to produce more ribosomes which would increase the amount and speed of protein synthesis. The availability of a greater number of ribosomes because of past stimulation might account for quick learning.

There are no learning experiments which are pertinent to this possibility; however, an experiment by Sidransky, Staehelin and Verney (1964) involving increased activity of the liver is somewhat pertinent. These individuals force-fed rats a purified diet devoid of the essential amino acid threonine for three days. Pathological changes occurred in the liver; accompanying these changes were greater RNA amounts and increased protein synthesis than was characteristic of control animals. The increased protein synthesis in the liver was related to enhanced activity of the ribosomes. The experimental animals showed polyribosomal aggregates of greater size than did the control animals. The data suggested that there was a marked shift in the size distribution of messenger RNA toward larger molecules or *a significant increase in the number of ribosomes for each messenger RNA strand*. If the latter interpretation is true for the liver in this increased activity state, it appears plausible that an increased number of ribosomes in polyribosomal aggregates in brain tissue might be operative during increased protein synthesis underlying learning and other behavior.

Another set of messenger RNA's produced would be for the synthesis of synaptic protein. The proteins synthesized would probably include ChA and AChE for the synthesis and degradation of ACh, one or more proteins which might be incorporated into synaptic membranes, one or more proteins which would increase the mass and area of pre- and/or postsynaptic endings, and maybe one or more proteins or enzymes which are functional in the activation of DNA sites. Some protein synthesized could be incorporated into membranes and other structures remote from the synapse.

The remaining messenger RNA, or RNA's, would be operative for lipid synthesis and transport; these lipids would be incorporated in membranes and elsewhere in the cell, probably in the gray matter of the brain. O'Brien (1965) reported that the lipids in gray matter showed a much higher turnover than those in myelin. Related to the difference in turnover rates are differences in structure: myelin contains one-fifth the molar proportion of polyunsaturated fatty acids that grey matter does and has ten times the amount of very long chain fatty acids than is found in grey matter. The presence of small chain and unsaturated fatty acids makes for low stability.

Sabesin and Isselbacher (1965) showed that proteins were essential for the transport of lipids in the vascular system, for the movement of lipids within the mucosal wall, and for their normal entry into the lymphatic system. Presumably, similar requirements would occur for intraneuronal movement of lipid.

During stimulation events DNA probably synthesizes mostly messenger RNA. Such synthesis of this RNA is suggested by the work of Hayashi and Spiegelman discussed above. This unstable RNA would be degraded soon after stimulation but could provide a small amount of protein before the stimulation ceased.

It is possible that some long-lived messenger RNA's might be activated by the electrochemical events during stimulation, thus precluding the need to activate DNA sites. The ultimate function of the RNA, however, would be to bring about protein synthesis.

Synaptic proteins would stream to the synapse following synthesis on ribosomes. Weiss (1960) indicated that there is a flow of material from the cell body to cell processes. Ochs reported similar results (1966). The flow has been estimated by Weiss as one millimeter (mm) per day; however, Ochs indicated greater rates, up to 70 mm per day. Most brain nerve cells have short processes and these rates would allow for some protein to reach some synapses quickly. Likewise, other proteins and enzymes would proceed to their cellular sites for their functions. A report by Barondes (1965) is consistent with these hypotheses. Using radioisotopes he found that the amount of labeled proteins in extracted nerve endings increased between two and 130 hours after injection. He interpreted these results as indicating that protein which was synthesized in the soma was transported by axoplasmic flow to the nerve ending.

The end result would be the degradation of some messenger RNA's but an increase in ribosomal RNA, synaptic and non-synaptic proteins, ribosomal protein and lipids. Thus the overall effect would be increased area in synaptic regions, increased activity of the ACh-AChE system, and an increase in the number of ribosomes. The increased area would necessitate increased amounts of the membrane constituents, proteins and lipids. The increased area would decrease the resistance at the synapse and allow for easier excitation of neural circuits subsequently. The lipid and protein membrane components could also affect extra-synaptic "tuning." A more important result might be that new connections would be effected by the increased growth. The increased activity of the ACh-CHE system would facilitate the excitation of neural circuits. The increase in ribosomes would make for an increase in the amount and rate of protein synthesis on subsequent occasions.

11) *Some synthesized protein is incorporated at the synapse so as to increase the functional contacts between nerve cells. Likewise, lipids and proteins synthesized for membrane structures would function to relate nerve cells in various parts of the brain and to affect cell permeability.*

The synthesized protein and lipids would stream to the

synapse or to membrane sites and be incorporated. This increased amount of protein and lipids at the synapse and in the membrane would cause the cortex to thicken and increase in weight if stimulation over long periods of time were involved. Thickening and increase in cortical weight has been reported by the California group but the procedures did not allow the investigators to determine in which specific cell structures these events were occurring. The visual cortex of the rat showed the greatest thickening and increase in weight.

12) *The increased functional contacts at synapses and via membrane changes facilitate activation of DNA sites by subsequent stimulation and may allow for further growth with new contacts to be formed.*

Growth of cells in the cerebral hemispheres is extensive even after conduction is possible (Gardner, 1963). Neurons increase in length and size through fetal life, infancy and childhood. Comparisons of certain cells at birth and in the adult show that marked changes occur in numbers and arrangements of dendritic processes in the intervening years. There is a decrease in the proportional volume of cell bodies and an increase in the proportional volume of dendrites (Schade and Pascoe, 1964); the surface area of dendrites increase whereas the surface area of cell bodies remain approximately the same after early infancy (Schade, Van Backen and Colon, 1964). These results show the importance of dendrites whose branches increase drastically over age. In the isolated cortex of kittens, prolific growth of recurrent axon collaterals have been observed (Sharpless, 1964). Part of the growth would be based on the fixed pattern development within a specific chemical environment as suggested above in Hypothesis 6. Other portions would develop through experiences in which stimulation brought about DNA activation with the resulting synthesis of RNA, proteins, and lipids. The difference between the two would be in the mechanisms regulating DNA activation. In the first case regulation would inhere in some way within the genetic code itself. In the latter, turning on the cistron would be through external environmental stimulation.

The neural growth would allow cells which were anatomically separated to decrease their distance because of the increased size and area of synaptic endings and dendritic processes. This event of decreasing the distance between neural cells would be facilitated by the respective cells being active at the same time and orienting toward one another. By electrical phenomena somewhat similar functional contacts would be effected via membrane changes.

The ultimate effect of the increased functional contacts would be to make DNA cistrons more receptive to activation. Activation in turn would make for more possible functional contacts or growth to occur. Thus a cycle of DNA activation and the establishing of functional contacts is set up.

13) *Relatively permanent memory, or symbolizing of experiences, is represented by activity in specific neural circuits which develop as a result of DNA activation.*

Experiences have been usually considered to be represented by growth at the synapse so that excitation in specific neural circuits could occur, e.g., the cell assemblies and phase sequences of Hebb. The nonsynaptic counterpart would be circuits connected via graded potentials such as suggested by Landauer. In the first case the synaptic proteins would be of great importance; in the latter, the lipids and proteins in membranes would be emphasized.

Another possible means of symbolizing experience is the DNA code itself. Both synaptic growth and tuning do occur but may merely facilitate the activation of DNA sites so that appropriate behavior can result. In this case DNA would contain not only the genetic code but the potential experiential code as well in that the latter would merely be the genetic code in operation. Thus learning would be a developmental or maturation problem in the same way as physical growth and development is.

The reader may instantly object to the hypothesis that experiential coding occurs via DNA. However, it is no more difficult to explain potential permanent memory as inherent in DNA than it is to explain why one linear sequence of bases in DNA should result in a complex organism such as man with so many precise features and capabilities whereas another sequence would effect a chimpanzee, rat, cat or planarian.

The synaptic and nonsynaptic connections between neural

units are ultimately responsible for coding experiences. However, DNA carries the expreiential code because the potential information for the multiple events for which an organism is capable is encoded in the linear sequence of bascs in DNA molecules, but internal or external environmental events trigger the activation of DNA sites such that RNA, proteins and lipids are synthesized for the cellular functions underlying the behavioral events. Thus, in this sense the DNA's are the *potential experiential coders* whereas the synaptic connections and nonsynaptic relationships are the *actualized experiential coders*. In the ultimate analysis memory would be the capacity of the total brain system with synaptic growths and graded potentials facilitating DNA activation.

The end result of the above is that the organism contains within his DNA molecules all the potential for learning and other psychological events and the environment merely brings these forth. Thus new learning is really not new! It is merely the actualization of something which has been present as a potential from conception.

14) *With increasing age the DNA complex is less receptive to activation; protein synthesis is less efficient, and the movement of protein to the synapse is less rapid. Thus elderly people, when confronted with a specific situation, can maintain the experience with difficulty only as long as reverberatory circuits are active. Little or no synaptic changes occur to facilitate DNA activation and to maintain the experience when removed from the event and thus, the experience is no longer retained. However, the individual has memory for experiences which transpired during previous years because nucleic acid and protein systems were more efficient. It is possible that not only may the macromolecular system be less efficient, but the internal environmental chemical changes required may be more difficult to effect.*

The results of Hyden (1961) and Cameron and Solyom (1961), cited in Chapters 8 and 9 are pertinent here. Hyden reported that the amount of RNA decreased in elderly individuals. Cameron and Solyom administered doses of DNA and of RNA to elderly patients with impaired memory ability. Only with RNA did memory improvement occur, and in some cases the improvement was great. When RNA doses were discontinued, memory impairment was again evident. Kral and Sved (1963) reported that RNase activity increased with age. This suggests that the decrement in RNA in older individuals could be due to the increased RNase activity. With a loss in RNA, proteins and other chemicals which are directly or indirectly dependent upon RNA synthesis would be affected. Thus the increased RNase activity could be responsible for the increased difficulty in the overall system from the DNA complex to the synapse.

Another deleterious anatomical aspect which aggravates the problem for older individuals is the decreasing number of neurons available. It has been estimated that the human loses 10,000 brain cells every day (which obviously are not replaced) and it is to be expected that intellectual ability decreases in later life (Curtis, 1963).

15) *Shock procedures quickly reduce the RNA content of the cell and prevent protein synthesis and the formation of memory traces.*

It is a common observation among clinicians that recent memory is impaired during shock treatments but permanent memory is unaffected. Furthermore, work by McGaugh, Pearlman and others discussed in Chapter 2 indicates that electrical shock and various other procedures interfere with the development of memory for recent events.

It has been indicated that during experimentally produced convulsions, i.e., with Metrazol and electric shock, the amount of RNA in brains of rats and cats increases slightly during the pre-convulsive phase but decreases to as much as 30 per cent within a few minutes. With this reduction of RNA, protein synthesis would be affected adversely as well. Gross decrements in ACh concentrations also occur, thus affecting the capability of neuron-neuron interactions. Furthermore, the drastic stimulation would be throughout the entire brain and prevent the coordination of the contributions of specific brain portions. The excessive stimulation probably would drastically modify the chemical range of the internal environment and would not be conducive to the formation of traces even if suitable RNA amounts were available.

16) *DNA complex modification in critical brain areas is*

facilitated by activity of the frontal-limbic system; however changes can occur in the complex with little contribution from this system, i.e., with low motivational tension. The activity in the frontal-limbic system is, likewise, dependent upon the development of the DNA complex in this system during previous experience.

The results of experiments on latent learning and incidental learning indicate that some learning can occur with low motivation. However, with increasing activity of the frontal-limbic system (up to a point) the probability of complex activation should increase. This increasing probability may be effected through changes in the chemical conditions of the internal environment bathing the molecules. Operation of this system may bring the chemical conditions within the narrow range required for change. The frontal-limbic system probably acts in intimate relationship with the reticular system in bringing out these changes. This change can be related to the changes in the EEG record.

17) *Quick learning, e.g., insightful learning, occurs because there were previous experiences with increased synaptic connections or nonsynaptic relationships available, as well as a greater number of ribosomes present, such that protein synthesis rates should be increased.*

Hebb (1949) suggested that insightful learning was possible for experienced animals, because many cell assemblies and phase sequences were available through synaptic growth to facilitate the acquisition of new cell assemblies and phase sequences. The present formulation would incorporate that possibility; however, the increased number of ribosomes would appear to provide a means for acquiring new synaptic growths quickly.

REACTIVATION AND FORGETTING

18) *Recall is effected by stimulation of portions of the neural units which have become functionally connected via synaptic growth or by membrane tuning as a result of DNA activation during a particular experience.*

After synaptic growth or tuning has linked together specific neural units, stimulation of portions of the unit by some of the stimulating elements of the previous experience can reactivate the total experience. Thus recall can be readily effected and can be elicited through external or internal triggering events.

Some individuals (e.g., Pribram, 1964) have spoken of recognition memory as an event which is different from the short and long term memories discussed above. However, recognition memory is merely the reactivation process in which the stimulus event which triggers the reactivation is external and in complete detail so that immediate reactivation occurs. On the other hand, much reactivation occurs in the absence of the total pattern of stimulation and requires activation of a portion of the neural circuitry so that the other portions can then be activated. Obviously, this is a more difficult process and is not immediate.

19) *In the process of recall new learning may be involved with DNA activation and protein synthesis occurring. Thus the memory trace is dynamic and changing during reactivation by new connections or relationships being formed. This process can lead to some degree of forgetting because the memory trace has changed.*

These ideas concerning a possible basis for the dynamic and static aspects of memories would handle well the common observation that memories have dynamic, changing aspects but have a basic, static portion as well. The changes would involve a cumulative process such that many of the original aspects are retained within the change. On the next occasion in which these same cells are stimulated through the operation of the same external stimulation, the organism's behavior may be modified also because of the intervening neurochemical events. However, even though the neural units may change (indicating the dynamic aspects of memory), the structure is still almost the same as it was before the change. Thus in the change of state of the neural complex, the basic aspects of the memory in the previous state is carried over in the next state. This aspect would stress sequential events as of prime importance. The basic aspects would be the static portion of memories.

20) *The synaptic and nonsynaptic growths are reversible and*

require further stimulation by previous stimuli, or portions of these, to become relatively permanent. If further stimulation is not provided the growth will eventually disappear and complete forgetting results.

The protein and lipids in the synaptic growth or membranes will be degraded periodically and new protein and lipid molecules are required. This event, obviously, requires that DNA be activated so that RNA and protein synthesis can be effected; some long-lived messenger RNA may be present to circumvent the need for frequent DNA activation. These degradation events provide for some forgetting to occur by disuse, a passive type of forgetting, whereas the previous hypothesis brings in an active type of forgetting, involving the interference effect of new learning on old learning.

21) . *The functioning of the various components of the brain through the neural circuits are usually readily available to the organism in the form of recall or in execution of motor patterns of behavior. However, in some cases these "traces" can be functionally excluded from their availability by the process of repression or other emotional events. Apparently the structures providing emotional tonicity operate to exclude previous experiences (and DNA complexes) from the availability of the integrating system.*

An example at a simple level is the capable student who becomes so emotionally upset during an examination that he forgets temporarily much that he has learned. Some types of unusual or selective forgetting is extremely difficult to explain on any level. An extreme example of this negative selectivity occurs in amnesia. The exact neurochemical basis for such events are obscure at the present time. However, these events appear to be related to the motivational aspects of the limbic system and to the sensory inhibition effects of the reticular system which have been uncovered by a number of investigators and discussed in Chapter 3.

A kind of possible positive selectivity is illustrated by memory functions under hypnosis. Some people have maintained that greater recall is present under hypnosis than during normal waking states. However, in some cases the accuracy of the recalled material has been questioned. Furthermore, some individuals have maintained that performance of subjects under hypnosis is essentially the same as performance under strong motivation (Barber, 1964). This would suggest that under hypnosis the frontal-limbic system provides emotional and motivational orientation in a certain direction, thus making available for recall the information contained within the specific brain structures involved.

INTEGRATION

22) *The overall neural integration for simple and complex behavior is provided by the brain stem reticular system with its projections to and from other portions of the brain, including the cortex. The neurochemical and neural modifications in the different areas of the brain allow for communication with other brain portions in some electrochemical manner via nerve impulses and electrical fields of force, and are integrated into specific behavior patterns through the operation of the reticular system.*

This emphasis on the reticular system as an integrator has been considered by a number of people and the ideas of Penfield expressed in the centrencephalic system (1956, 1958, 1960) and those of Jasper (1956, 1958) are especially pertinent. However, the frontal lobes and limbic system probably contribute to the overall integration involving sequential events (Pribram, 1960). This latter system probably also contributes motivational and emotional components to the process. These contributions would be maintained by the potential explicit in the DNA complex which is affected by environmental stimulation so that protein synthesis and synaptic growth and membrane changes can occur. However, as stated above, the DNA complex which would be receptive to activation in the reticular system would not be the same ones which are receptive in the frontal-limbic system; these latter would, in turn, be different than those in the motor systems, etc. Thus each specialized portion of the brain would perform its function through the operation of different DNA sites in the chromosomes of the nerve cell.

In summary, the above hypotheses are suggesting that stimulation of specific nerve cells in a particular portion of the brain causes a modification in DNA complex such that DNA is activated to synthesize RNA. Four types of RNA are synthesized: messenger (s) for synaptic and nonsynaptic protein, messenger (s) for ribosomal protein, messenger (s) for enzymes to synthesize lipids and ribosomal RNA. The first protein proceeds to synaptic junctions to increase the surface area, to make for the development of connections with other nerve cells and to make postsynaptic neurons more susceptible to excitation. The lipids are incorporated along with proteins into membranes at the synapse and elsewhere. The ribosomal RNA and protein aggregate to make new ribosmes. The synaptic changes link together neural circuits to make more probable the inclusion of certain cells in the electrochemical stimulation which results from the physical energies impinging upon the receptors of the organism when external stimulation occurs. This stimulation allows the DNA complex in a greater number of nerve cells to be potentially available for modification so that further protein synthesis can occur. The ribosomes which function as vehicles for protein synthesis make for more rapid rate of protein synthesis during later stimulation. Reactivation involves stimulation of a portion of neural circuits. Forgetting is of three types. One involves an interference mechanism because in reactivation new synaptic and nonsynaptic relationships are being made and memory is gradually changing. Other forgetting occurs because synaptic and nonsynaptic growths are reversible, i.e., proteins and lipids are degraded and need to be replenished through stimulation events. The last type occurs because certain brain systems inhibit the functioning of other systems. Overall integration is of an intercellular nature with the upper reticular system coordinating the contributions of the neural circuits in the various brain areas.

The above discussion has utilized the main difference between neural and nonneural tissue, the occurrence of synapses in the former as probably representing an important functional site as well as the information indicating that RNA, proteins and lipids increase during functional activity. The hypotheses represent a plausible, speculative set of neurochemical and neurological hypotheses relative to the problem of brain function. It is specific in some spots and vague in others; it is far from complete and contains many gaps. For example, it is obvious that in the development of memory traces during learning events there is a sequence of events, $a, b, c, \ldots$ in which a is the stimulation of peripheral receptors, and b is the first order transformation, i.e., the occurrence of nerve impulses. In this sequence, an important event, say g, is that DNA is activated to synthesize particular RNA (h) for protein synthesis (i), and a number of other events occur. We know little about the total sequence but it appears safe to say that DNA activation with associated RNA and protein synthesis is an important portion. Speculation concerning the events leading to g and following i are hazardous; however, some of these have been attempted. In any event, these speculations represent a logical starting point in the search for the molecular neurochemical changes which are related to learning and other behavior.

An alternative possibility to the DNA activation scheme for learning events is that DNA is not activated but that certain existing RNA species are made more resistant to degradation by RNase. This result has occurred for transfer RNA in plants when treated with certain hormones (Bendana and Galston, 1965). The end result would be an increase in protein synthesis as in DNA activation. The positive results in some of the RNA injection experiments could be consistent with this possibility also. It is possible that both mechanisms are occurring in learning events: some DNA sites may be active for the synthesis of certain RNA species whereas other RNA species could be stabilized by the electrochemical events involved in learning.

One aspect that the present formulation has avoided is the role of glia in behavior. Hyden, Galambos, Landauer and Pribram have assigned these cells a primary function in learning events. We prefer to speak grossly of neural structures at this stage until more conclusive work is available even though Hyden's results are both interesting and suggestive.

Although speculations are hazardous, some of the main hypotheses can be tested with present techniques. One main assumption of the present approach is that increases in ribosomes and ribosomal RNA and protein should result from environmental stimulation involving learning over a period of time. Some data from molecular biology tends to suggest this. However, this could be tested directly. One would first determine the brain areas which show increased RNA synthesis during the specific tasks of concern by training one group of animals for a long period of time while depriving a second set of animals. In a later similar experiment, the ribosomes would be extracted from the specific brain site of both groups of animals and compared. The trained group should show a greater number of ribosomes and greater amounts of ribosomal RNA and ribosomal protein than the deprived group.

As a corroborative procedure, radioactive material containing, for example, C^{14}, could be injected into animals at the beginning of the experiment. After the training period both ribosomal RNA and protein should show greater evidence of the label in trained animals than in the deprived animals. Furthermore, the synaptic endings could be separated by differential centrifugation, as done by de Robertis, and the amount of label determined. Obviously, the above hypotheses are indicating that greater labeling should occur in the trained animals.

REFERENCES

ADAMS, H. E., and LEWIS, D. J.: Electroconvulsive shock, retrograde amnesia, and competing responses. *J. Comp. Physiol. Psychol., 55:* 302, 1962.

ADEY, W. R.: Organization of the rhinencephalon. In H. H. Jasper, L. P. Proctor, R. S. Knighton, W. C. Noshay, and R. T. Costello (Eds.), *Reticular Formation of the Brain*. Boston, Little, Brown, 1958.

ADEY, W. R.: Instrumentation of nervous system for studies of behavior and performance in space flight. Paper presented at Fifth National Symposium on Space Electronics and Telemetry, Washington, D. C., September 1960.

ADEY, W. R., DUNLOP, C. W., and HENDRIX, C. E.: Hippocampal slow waves. *Arch. Neurol.* (Chicago), *3:*74, 1960.

AGRANOFF, B. W., and KLINGER, P. D.: Puromycin effect on memory fixation in goldfish. *Science, 146:*952, 1964.

ALFERT, M.: Some cytochemical contributions to genetic chemistry. In W. P. McElroy and R. Glass (Eds.), *The Chemical Basis of Heredity*. Baltimore, John Hopkins Press, 1957.

ALLFREY, V. G., FAULKNER, R., and MIRSKY, A. E.: Acetylation and methylation of histones and their possible role in the regulation of RNA synthesis. *Proc. Nat. Acad. Sci., 51:*786, 1964.

ALLFREY, V. G., and MIRSKY, A. E.: Structural modifications of histones and their possible role in the regulation of RNA synthesis. *Science, 144:*559 (abstract). 1964 (a).

ALLFREY, V. G., and MIRSKY, A. E.: Role of histone in nuclear function. In J. Bonner and P.Ts'O (Eds.), *The Nucleohistones*. San Francisco, Holden-Day, 1964 (b).

ALTMAN, J.: Are new neurons formed in the brains of adult mammals? *Science, 135:*1127, 1962.

ALTMAN, J.: Autoradiographic investigation of cell proliferation in the brains of rats and cats. *Anat. Rec., 145:*573, 1963 (a).

ALTMAN, J.: Differences in the utilization of tritiated leucine by single neurons in normal and exercised rats: an autoradiographic investigation with micro-densitometry. *Nature, 199:*777, 1963 (b).

ALTMAN, J.: Autoradiography. In J. Gaito (Ed.), *Macromolecules and Behavior*. New York: Appleton-Century-Crofts, 1966.

199

200 *Molecular Psychobiology*

APPEL, S.: A critical appraisal of the role of RNA in information storage in the nervous system. Paper presented at the Kansas State University symposium, *Role of Macromolecules in Complex Behavior,* April 1964.

AVERY, O. T., MacLEOD, C. M., and McCARTY, M.: Studies on the chemical nature of the substance inducing transformation of pneumococcal types. Induction of transformation by a deoxyribonucleic acid fraction isolated from Pneumococcus Type III. *J. Exp. Med., 79:*137, 1944.

BARBER, T. X.: Toward a theory of pain: relief of chronic pain by prefrontal leucotomy, opiates, placebos, and hypnosis. *Psychol. Bull., 56:*430, 1959.

BARBER, T. X.: Hypnotizability, suggestibility, and personality: V. A critical review of research findings. *Psychol. Rep., 14:*229, 1964.

BARONDES, S. H.: Delayed appearance of labeled protein in isolated nerve endings and axoplasmic flow. *Science, 146:*779, 1964.

BARONDES, S. H.: Relationship of biological regulatory mechanisms to learning and memory. *Nature, 205:*18, 1965.

BARONDES, S. H., DINGMAN, W., and SPORN, M. B.: *In vitro* stimulation of protein synthesis by liver nuclear RNA. *Nature, 196:*145, 1962.

BARONDES, S. H., and JARVIK, M. E.: The influences of actinomycin-D on brain RNA synthesis and on memory. *J. Neurochem., 11:*187, 1964.

BARANOV, M. N., and PEVZNER, L. Z.: Microchemical and microspectrophotometric studies on the intralaminar distribution of nucleic acids in the brain cortex under various experimental conditions. *J. Neurochem., 10:*279, 1963.

BAXTER, C. F., and ROBERTS, R.: Gamma-aminobutyric acid and cerebral metabolism. In R. O. Brady and D. B. Tower (Eds.), *The Neurochemistry of Nucleotides and Amino Acids.* New York, Wiley, 1960.

BEAVEN, G. H., HOLIDAY, E. R., and JOHNSON, E. A.: Optical properties of nucleic acids and their components. In E. Chargaff and J. N. Davidson (Eds.), *The Nucleic Acids,* New York, Academic Press, 1955, Vol. 1.

BECKWITH, W. C.: *Some Biochemical Correlates of Imprinting.* Paper presented during American Psychological Association meetings in St. Louis, Missouri, 1962.

BEER, M.: Electron microscopy of unbroken DNA Molecules. *J. Molec. Biol., 3:*263, 1961.

BEERMAN, W., and CLEVER, U.: Chromosome puffs. *Sci. Amer., 210:* 50, 1964.

BELOZERSKY, A. N., and SPIRIN, A. S.: Chemistry of the nucleic acids of micro-organisms. In E. Chargaff and J. N. Davidson (Eds.), *The Nucleic Acids.* New York, Academic Press, 1960, Vol. 3.

BENDANA, F. E., and GALSTON, A. W.: Hormone-induced stabilization of soluble RNA in pea-stem tissue. *Science, 150:*69, 1965.

BENDICH, A., RUSSELL, P. J., and BROWN, G. B.: On the heterogeneity of the deoxyribonucleic acids. *J. Biol. Chem., 203:*305, 1953.

BENNETT, E. L., DIAMOND, M. C., KRECH, D., and ROSENZWEIG, M. R.: Chemical and anatomical plasticity of brain. *Science, 146:*610, 1964.

BENNETT, E. L., KRECH, D., ROSENZWEIG, M. R., KARLSSON, H., DYE, N., and OHLANDER, A.: Cholinesterase and lactic dehydrogenase activity in the rat brain. *J. Neurochem., 3:*153, 1958.

BENNETT, E. L., ROSENZWEIG, M. R., KRECH, D. R., KARLSSON, H., DYE, N., and OHLANDER, A.: Individual, strain and age differences in cholinesterase activity of the rat brain. *J. Neurochem., 3:*144, 1958.

BENZER, S.: On the topography of the genetic fine structure. *Proc. Nat. Acad. Sci., 47:*403, 1961.

BENZER, S.: The fine structure of the gene. *Sci. Amer., 206:*70, 1962.

BEXTON, W. H., HERON, W., and SCOTT, T. H.: Effects of decreased variation in the sensory environment. *Canad. J. Psychol., 8:*70, 1954.

BILLEN, D., and HNILICA, L. S.: Inhibition of DNA synthesis by histones. In *The Nucleohistones.* San Francisco, Holden Day, 1964.

BIRNSTIEL, M. L., and FLAMM, W. G.: Intranuclear site of histone synthesis. *Science, 115:*1435, 1964.

BIRNSTIEL, M. L., FLEISSNER, E., and BOREK, E.: Nucleolus: a center of RNA methylation. *Science, 142:*1577, 1963.

BLOCH, D. P.: Genetic implications of histone behavior. *J. Cell. Comp. Physiol., 62:*87, 1963.

BOLTON, E. T., and McCARTHY, B. J.: A general method for the isolation of RNA complementary to DNA. *Proc. Nat. Acad. Sci., 48:* 1390, 1962.

BONAVITA, V., BONASERA, N., ZITO, M., and SCARANO, E.: Electrophysiological and neurochemical studies following injection of mononucleotides and their derivatives. *J. Neurochem., 10:*155, 1963.

BONNER, J.: The molecular biology of memory. Paper presented at the Kansas State University symposium, *Role of Macromolecules in Complex Behavior,* April 1964.

BONNER, J.: The next new biology. *Plant Sci. Bull., 11:*1, 1965.

BONNER, J.: Molecular biological approaches to the study of memory. In J. Gaito (Ed.), *Macromolecules and Behavior.* New York, Appleton-Century-Crofts, 1966.

BONNER, J., and HUANG, R. C.: Properties of chromosomal nucleo-histone. *J. Molec. Biol., 6:*169, 1962 (a).

BONNER, J., and HUANG, R. C.: Chromosomal control of enzyme synthesis. *Canad. J. Botany., 40:*1487, 1962 (b).

BONNER, J., and HUANG, R. C.: Role of histone in chromosomal RNA synthesis. In J. Bonner and P. Ts'O (Eds.), *The Nucleohistones.* San Francisco, Holden-Day, 1964.

BONNER, J., and TS'O, P. (Eds.): *The Nucleohistones.* San Francisco, Holden-Day, 1964.

BRAZIER, M. A. B.: Long-persisting electrical traces in the brain of man and their possible relationship to higher nervous activity. *EEG Journal,* Suppl. *13:*347, 1960.

BREMER, F.: Central regulatory mechanisms—introduction. In H. W. Magoun (Ed.), *Handbook of Physiology—Neurophysiology, Vol. II.* Baltimore, Williams and Wilkins, 1960.

BRIGGS, M. H., and KITTO, G. B.: The molecular basis of memory and learning. *Psychol. Rev., 69:*537, 1962.

BRIZZEE, K. R., VOGT, J., and KHARETCHKO, X.: Postnatal changes in glia/neuron index with a comparison of methods of cell enumeration in the white rat. In D. P. Purpura and J. P. Schade (Eds.), *Growth and Maturation of the Brain.* New York, Elsevier, 1964.

BROADBENT, D. E.: A mechanical model for human attention and immediate memory. *Psychol. Rev., 64:*205, 1957.

BROADHURST, P. L.: Applications of biometrical genetics to the inheritance of behavior. In H. J. Eysenck (Ed.), *Experiments in Personality, Vol. 1, Psychogenetics and Psychopharmacology.* New York, Humanities Press, 1960.

BROOKHART, J. M.: The cerebellum. In H. W. Magoun (Ed.), *Handbook of Physiology-Neurophysiology, Vol. II.* Baltimore, Williams and Wilkins, 1960.

BROWN, G. B., and ROLL, P. M.: Biosynthesis of nucleic acids. In E. Chargaff and J. N. Davidson (Eds.), *The Nucleic Acids, Vol. II.* New York, Academic Press, 1955.

BULLOCK, T. H.: Neurophysiology: United States-Japan joint symposium. *Science, 144:*1361, 1964.

BURES, J., and BURESOVA, O.: Cortical spreading depression as a memory disturbing factor. *J. Comp. Physiol. Psychol., 56:*268, 1963.

BURNS, B. D.: The promotion of after-bursts in isolated unanesthetized cerebral cortex. *J. Physiol., 125:*427, 1954.

BURNS, B. D.: *The Mammalian Cerebral Cortex.* London, England, Arnold, 1958.

BUSCH, H.:*Histones and Other Nuclear Proteins.* New York, Academic Press, 1965.

BUSCH, H., STARBUCK, W. C., SINGH, E. J., and RO, T. S.: Chromosomal proteins. In M. Locke (Ed.), *The Role of Chromosomes in Development.* New York, Academic Press, 1964.

BUSCH, H., STEELE, W. J., HNILICA, L. S., and TAYLOR, C.: Metabolism of histones. In J. Bonner and P. Ts'o (Eds.), *The Nucleohistones.* San Francisco, Holden-Day, 1964.

BUSCH, H., STEELE, W. J., HNILICA, L. S., TAYLOR, C. W., and MAVIOGLU, H.: Biochemistry of histones and the cell cycle. *J. Cell. Comp. Physiol., 62:*95, 1963.

BUSH, R. R., and MOSTELLER, F.: *Stochastic Models for Learning.* New York, Wiley, 1955.

BUTLER, J. A. V.: *Inside the Living Cell.* New York, Basic Books, 1959.

BYRNE, R., LEVIN, J. G., BLADEN, H. A., and NIRENBERG, M. W.: The *in vitro* formation of a DNA-ribosome complex. *Proc. Nat. Acad. Sci., 52:*140, 1964.

CAMERON, D. E.: The processes of remembering. *Brit. J. Psychiat., 109:*325, 1963.

CAMERON, D. E., and SOLYOM, F.: Effects of ribonucleic acid on memory. *Geriatrics, 16:*74, 1961.

CAMERON, D. E., SOLYOM, L., SVED, S., and WAINRIB, B.: *Effects of Intravenous Administration of Ribonucleic Acid upon Failure of Memory for Recent Events in Presenile and Aged Individuals.* Unpublished paper, Royal Victoria Hospital, Montreal, Canada, 1962.

CANNON, M., KRUG, R., and GILBERT, W.: The binding of S-RNA by *Escherichia coli* ribosomes. *J. Molec. Biol., 7:*360, 1963.

CHAMBERLAIN, T. J., HOLICK, P., and GERARD, R. W.: Fixation of experience in the rat spinal cord. *J. Neurophysiol., 26:*662, 1963.

CHAMBERLAIN, T. J., ROTHSCHILD, G. H., and GERARD, R. W.: Drugs affecting RNA and learning. *Proc. Nat. Acad. Sci., 49:*918, 1963.

CHANG, H. T.: The evoked potentials. In J. Field (Ed.), *Handbook of*

Physiology—Neurophysiology, Vol. 1. Baltimore, Williams and Wilkins, 1959.

CHARGAFF, E.: Isolation and composition of the deoxypentose nucleic acids and of the corresponding nucleoproteins. In E. Chargaff and J. N. Davidson (Eds.), *The Nucleic Acids, Vol. I.* New York, Academic Press, 1955.

CHIPCHASE, M. I. H., and BIRNSTIEL, M. L.: On the nature of nucleolar RNA. *Proc. Nat. Acad. Sci., 50:*1101, 1963.

CHITRE, V. S., CHOPRA, S. P., and TALWAR, G. P.: Changes in the ribonucleic acid content of the brain during experimentally induced convulsions. *J. Neurochem., 11:*439, 1964.

CHITRE, V. S., and TALWAR, G. P.: Correlation of electrical activity of brain with metabolic parameters. Part II. Pentose nucleic acid content of isolated cerebral cortex during various phases of electrical activity following topical application of Metrazol. *Indian J. Med. Res., 51:*80, 1963.

COLEMAN, J. C.: *Abnormal Psychology and Modern Life.* Chicago, Scott, Foresman, 1956.

COMB, D. G., BROWN, R., and KATZ, S.: The nuclear DNA and RNA components of the aquatic fungus *Blastocladiella emersonii. J. Molec. Biol., 8:*781, 1964.

COMB, D. G., and KATZ, S.: Studies on the biosynthesis and methylation of transfer RNA. *J. Molec. Biol., 8:*790, 1964.

COOK, L., DAVIDSON, A. B., DAVIS, D. J., GREEN, H., and FELLOWS, E. J.: Ribonucleic acid: effect on conditioned behavior in rats. *Science, 141:*268, 1963.

COONS, E. E., and MILLER, N. E.: Conflict versus consolidation of memory traces to explain "retrograde amnesia" produced by ECS. *J. Comp. Physiol. Psychol., 53:*524, 1960.

CORNING, W. C., and JOHN, E. R.: Effect of ribonuclease on retention of conditioned response in regenerated planarians. *Science, 134:* 1363, 1961.

COSTA, E.: Brain research. *Science, 148:*865, 1965.

CRAFTS, L. W., SCHNEIRLA, T. C., ROBINSON, E. E., and GILBERT, R. W.: *Recent Experiments in Psychology.* New York, McGraw-Hill, 1950.

CRICK, F. H. C.: The structure of the heredity material. *Sci. Amer., 191:*54, 1954.

CRICK, F. H. C.: Nucleic acids. *Sci. Amer., 197:*188, 1957.

CRICK, F. H. C.: The genetic code. *Sci. Amer., 207:*66, 1962.

CRICK, F. H. C.: On the genetic code. *Science, 139:*461, 1963.

CRICK, F. H. C., BARNETT, L., BRENNER, S., and WATTS-TOBIN, R. J.: General nature of the genetic code for proteins. *Nature, 192:*1227, 1961.

CURTIS, H. J.: Biological mechanisms underlying the aging process. *Science, 141:*686, 1963.

DATTA, R. K., and GHOSH, J. J.: Studies on the stability of brain cortex ribosomes. *J. Neurochem., 11:*595, 1964.

DAVID, P. R., and SNYDER, L. H.: Some interrelations between psychology and genetics. In S. Koch (Ed.), *Psychology: A study of a Science, Vol. IV, Biologically Oriented Fields: Their place in Psychology and in Biological Science.* New York, McGraw-Hill, 1962.

DAVIDSON, E. H.: Hormones and genes. *Sci. Amer., 212:*36, 1965.

DELAYFRESNAYE, J. F. (Ed.): *Brain mechanisms and Consciousness.* Oxford, Blackwell, 1956.

DE ROBERTIS, E., DE IRALDI, A. P., DE LORES ARNAIZ, G. R., and SALGANICOFF, L.: Cholinergic and non-cholinergic nerve endings in rat brain—I. Isolation and subcellular distribution of acetylcholine and acetylcholinesterase. *J. Neurochem., 9:*23, 1962.

DE ROBERTIS, E., DE LORES ARNAIZ, G. R., SALGANICOFF, L., DE IRALDI, A. P., and ZIEHER, L. M.: Isolation of synaptic vesicles and structural organization of the acetylcholine system within brain nerve endings. *J. Neurochem., 10:*225, 1963.

DE ROBERTIS, E., SALGANICOFF, L., ZIEHER, L. M., and DE LORES ARNAIZ, G. R.: Acetylcholine and cholineacetylase content of synaptic vesicles. *Science, 140:*300, 1963.

DETHIER, V. G., and STELLAR, E.: *Animal Behavior.* Englewood Cliffs, Prentice-Hall, 1961.

DIAMOND, M. C., KRECH, D., and ROSENZWEIG, M. R.: The effects of an enriched environment on the histology of the rat cerebral cortex. *J. Comp. Neurol., 123:*111, 1964.

DI GIROLAMO, A., HENSHAW, E. C., and HIATT, H. H.: Messenger ribonucleic acid in rat liver nuclei and cytoplasm. *J. Molec. Biol., 8:* 479, 1964.

DINGMAN, W., and SPORN, M. B.: The incorporation of 8-azaguanine into rat brain RNA and its effect on maze-learning by the rat: an inquiry into the biochemical bases of memory. *J. Psychiat. Res., 1:* 1, 1961.

DINGMAN, W., and SPORN, M. B.: The isolation and physical characterization of nuclear and microsomal ribonucleic acid from rat brain and liver. *Bioch. Biophy. Acta., 61:*164, 1962.

206 *Molecular Psychobiology*

Dingman, W., and Sporn, M. B.: Molecular theories of memory. *Science, 144*:26, 1964.

Dobzhansky, T.: *Mankind Evolving.* New Haven, Yale Univ. Press, 1962.

Duncan, C. P.: Retroactive effect of electroshock on learning. *J. Comp. Physiol. Psychol., 42*:32, 1949.

Dunn, D. B., and Smith, J. D.: Incorporation of halogenated pyrmidines into the deoxyribonucleic acids of *Bacterium coli* and its bacteriophages. *Nature, 174*:305, 1954.

Dure, L., and Waters, L.: Long-lived messenger RNA: evidence from cotton seed germination. *Science, 147*:410, 1965.

Eccles, J. C.: The physiology of imagination. *Sci. Amer., 199*:135, 1958.

Eccles, J. C.: Neuron physiology—introduction. In J. Field (Ed.), *Handbook of Physiology-Neurophysiology. Vol. III.* Baltimore, Williams and Wilkins, 1959.

Eck, R. V.: Genetic code: emergence of a symmetrical pattern. *Science, 140*:477, 1963.

Edstrom, A.: Effect of spinal cord transection on the base composition and content of RNA in the Mauthner nerve fibre of the goldfish. *J. Neurochem., 11*:557, 1964.

Edstrom, J. E.: Chromosomal RNA and other nuclear RNA fractions. In M. Locke (Ed.), *The Role of Chromosomes in Development.* New York, Academic Press, 1964.

Egyhazi, E., and Hyden, H.: Experimentally induced changes in the base composition of the ribonucleic acids of isolated nerve cells and their oligodendroglial cells. *J. Biophys. Biochem. Cytol., 10*:403, 1961.

Estes, W. K.: Toward a statistical theory of learning. *Psychol. Rev., 57*:94, 1950.

Fisher, A. E.: Chemical stimulation of the brain. *Sci. Amer., 210*:60, 1964.

Fjerdingstad, E. J., Nissen, T., and Roigaard-Petersen, H. H.: Effect of ribonucleic acid (RNA) extracted from the brain of trained animals on learning in rats. *Scand. J. Psychol., 6*:1, 1965.

Flexner, J. B., Flexner, L. B., and Stellar, E.: Memory in mice as affected by intracerebral puromycin. *Science, 141*:57, 1963.

Flexner, L. B.: Physiologic development of the cortex of the brain and its relationship to its morphology, chemical constitution, and enzyme systems. In S. Cobb (Ed.), *The Biology of Mental Health and Disease.* New York, Hoeber, 1952.

FLEXNER, L. B., FLEXNER, J. B., ROBERTS, R. B., and DE LA HABA, G.: Loss of recent memory in mice as related to regional inhibition of cerebral protein synthesis. *Proc. Nat. Acad. Sci., 52*:1165, 1964.

FLEXNER, L. B., FLEXNER, J. B., DE LA HABA, G., and ROBERTS, R. B.: Loss of memory as related to inhibition of cerebral protein synthesis. *J. Neurochem., 12*:535, 1965.

FREESE, A. B.: Transitions and transversions induced by depurinating agents. *Proc. Nat. Acad. Sci., 47*:540, 1961.

FRENSTER, J. H., ALLFREY, B. G., and MIRSKY, A. E.: Repressed and active chromatin isolated from interphase lymphocytes. *Proc. Nat. Acad. Sci., 50*:1026, 1963.

FUSTER, J. M.: Effects of stimulation of brain stem on tachistoscopic perception. *Science, 127*:150, 1958.

GAITO, J.: A neuropsychological approach to thinking. *Psychol. Rep., 4*:323, 1958.

GAITO, J.: A biochemical approach to learning and memory. *Psychol. Rev., 68*:288, 1961.

GAITO, J.: DNA and RNA as memory molecules. *Psychol. Rev., 70*: 471, 1963 (a) .

GAITO, J.: *Nucleic Acids and Behavior.* Mimeographed paper, Kansas State University, June, 1963 (b) .

GALAMBOS, R.: A glia-neural theory of brain function. *Proc. Nat. Acad. Sci., 47*:129, 1961.

GALAMBOS, R., and MORGAN, C. T.: The neural basis of learning. In J. Field (Ed.) , *Handbook of Physiology-Neurophysiology, Vol. III.* Baltimore, Williams and Wilkins, 1960.

GARDNER, E.: *Fundamentals of Neurology.* Philadelphia, Saunders, 1963.

GASTAUT, H.: The role of the reticular formation in establishing conditioned reactions. In H. H. Jasper, L. P. Proctor, R. S. Knighton, W. C. Noshay, and R. T. Costello (Eds.) , *Reticular Formation of the Brain.* Boston, Little, Brown, 1958.

GEIGER, A.: Chemical changes accompanying activity in the brain. In D. Richter (Ed.) , *Metabolism of the Nervous System.* London, Pergamon Press, 1957.

GEIGER, A., YAMASOKI, S., and LYONS, R.: Changes in nitrogenous components of brain produced by stimulation of short duration. *Amer. J. Physiol., 184*:239, 1956.

GERARD, R. W.: What is memory? *Sci. Amer., 189*:118, 1953.

GERARD, R. W.: Neurophysiology: An integration (molecules, neurons, and behavior). In J. Field (Ed.), *Handbook of Physiology-Neurophysiology. Vol. III*. Baltimore, Williams and Wilkins, 1960.

GERARD, R. W.: The material basis of memory. *J. Verbal Learning Verbal Behavior, 2*:22, 1963.

GERARD, R. W., CHAMBERLAIN, T. J., and ROTHSCHILD, G. H.: RNA in learning and memory. *Science, 140*:381, 1963.

GERBRANDT, L. K., and THOMSON, C. W.: Competing response and amnesic effects of electroconvulsive shock under extinction and incentive shifts. *J. Comp. Physiol. Psychol., 58*:208, 1964.

GIBOR, A., and GRANICK, S.: Plastids and mitochondria: inheritable systems. *Science, 145*:890, 1964.

GILLESPIE, D., and SPIEGELMAN, S.: A quantitative assay for DNA-RNA hybrids with DNA immobilized on a membrane. *J. Molec. Biol., 12*:829, 1965.

GLICKMAN, S. E.: Deficits in avoidance learning produced by stimulation of the ascending reticular formation. *Canad. J. Psychol., 12*: 97, 1958.

GLICKMAN, S. E.: Perseverative neural processes and consolidation of the memory trace. *Psychol. Bull., 58*:218, 1961.

GODDARD, G. V.: Functions of the amygdala. *Psychol. Bull., 62*:89, 1964.

GOLDBERG, A. L.: Memory mechanisms. *Science, 144*:1529, 1964.

GOLDBERG, I. H., RABINOWITZ, M., and REICH, E.: Basis of actinomycin action, I. DNA binding and inhibition of RNA-polymerase syntheic reactions by actinomycin. *Proc. Nat. Acad. Sci., 48*:2094, 1962.

GOLDSTEIN, K.: *Language and Language Disturbances*. New York, Grune and Stratton, 1948.

GOMATOS, P. J., and TAMM, J.: The secondary structure of reovirus RNA. *Proc. Nat. Acad. Sci., 49*:707, 1963.

GOODMAN, H. M., and RICH, A.: Formation of a DNA-soluble RNA hybrid and its relation to the origin, evolution, and degeneracy of soluble RNA. *Proc. Nat. Acad. Sci., 48*:2101, 1962.

GOODWIN, B. C., and SIZER, I. W.: Histone regulation of lactic dehydrogenase in embryonic chick brain tissue. *Science, 148*:242, 1965.

GRAMPP, W., and EDSTROM, J. E.: The effect of nervous activity on ribonucleic acid of the crustacean receptor neurons. *J. Neurochem., 10*:725, 1963.

GRANICK, S.: Cytoplasmic units of inheritance. *Science, 147*:911, 1965.

GRASTYAN, A.: The hippocampus and nervous activity. In M. A. B.

Brazier (Ed.), *Central Nervous System and Behavior*. New York, Macy, 1959.

GREEN, J. D.: The hippocampus. In J. Field (Ed.), *Handbook of Physiology-Neurophysiology, Vol. II.* Baltimore, Williams and Wilkins, 1960.

GROSS, C. G., and CAREY, F. M.: Transfer of learned response by RNA injection: failure of attempts to replicate. *Science, 150:*1749, 1965.

GROSSMAN, S. P.: A neuropharmacological analysis of the role of limbic and reticular mechanisms in motivation and learning. *Bol. Inst. Estud. Med. Biol., (Mex.), 22:*115, 1964.

GRUMBACH, M. M., MORISHIMA, A., and TAYLOR, J. H.: Human sex chromosome abnormalities in relation to DNA replication and heterochromatinization. *Proc. Nat. Acad. Sci., 49:*581, 1963.

GRUNBERG-MANAGO, M.: Enzymatic synthesis of nucleic acids. In *Progress in Biophysics, Vol. XIII.* New York, Pergamon Press, 1963.

GRUNDFEST, H.: Synaptic and ephaptic transmission. In J. Field (Ed.), *Handbook of Physiology-Neurophysiology, Vol. III.* Baltimore, Williams and Wilkins, 1959.

GUZMAN-FLORES, C., OLEARAZ, M., SALAS, M., and PACHECO, P.: Correlation of EEG activity and behavior in split-brain cats. *Bol. Inst. Etud. Med. Biol. (Mex.), 23:*17, 1965.

HALL, B. J., and SPIEGLMAN, S.: Sequence complementarity of T2-DNA and T2-specific RNA. *Proc. Nat. Acad. Sci., 47:*137, 1961.

HALSTEAD, W. C.: Brain and intelligence. In L. A. Jeffress (Ed.), *Cerebral Mechanisms in Behavior*. New York, Wiley, 1951.

HANDSCHUMACHER, R. E., and WELCH, A. D.: Agents which influence nucleic acid metabolism. In E. Chargaff and J. N. Davidson (Eds.), *The Nucleic Acids, Vol. III.* New York: Academic Press, 1960.

HARDESTY, B., MILLER, R., and SCHWETT, R.: Polyribosome breakdown and hemoglobin synthesis. *Proc. Nat. Acad. Sci., 50:*924, 1963.

HAY, E. D., and REVEL, J. P.: The fine structure of the DNP component of the nucleus. *J. Cell. Biol., 16:*29, 1963.

HAYASHI, M., HAYASHI, M. N., and SPIEGELMAN, S.: Replicating form of a single-stranded DNA virus: isolation and properties. *Science, 140:*1313, 1963.

HAYASHI, M., SPIEGELMAN, S., FRANKLIN, N. C., and LURIA, S. E.: Separation of the RNA message transcribed in response to a specific inducer. *Proc. Nat. Acad. Sci., 49:*729, 1963.

HEAD, H.: *Aphasia and Kindred Disorders of Speech*. New York, Macmillan, 1926.

HEBB, D. O.: *The Organization of Behavior*. New York, Wiley, 1949.

HEBB, D. O.: Drives and the CNS (Conceptual nervous system). *Psychol. Rev., 62:*243, 1955.

HEBB, D. O.: Instinctive features of learning in the higher animal. In J. F. Delayfresnaye (Ed.), *Brain Mechanisms and Learning.* Oxford, Blackwell, 1961.

HECHTER, O., and HALKERSTON, I. D. K.: Effects of steroid hormones on gene regulation and cell metabolism. In V. E. Hall, A. C. Giese, and R. R. Sonnenschein (Eds.), *Annual Review of Physiology, Vol. XXVII.* Palo Alto, Annual Reviews, 1965.

HENNEY, H. R., JR., and STORCK, R.: Polyribosomes and morphology in *Neurospora crassa. Proc. Nat. Acad. Sci., 51:*1050, 1964.

HERNANDEZ-PEON, R.: Reticular mechanisms of sensory control. In W. A. Rosenblith (Ed.), *Sensory Communication.* New York, Wiley, 1961.

HERON, W.: The pathology of boredom. *Sci. Amer., 196:*52, 1957.

HERON, W., DOANE, B. K., and SCOTT, T. H.: Visual disturbances after prolonged perceptual isolation. *Canad. J. Psychol., 10:*13, 1956.

HESS, E. H.: Imprinting in birds. *Science, 146:*1128, 1964.

HNILICA, L. S., TAYLOR, C. W., and BUSCH, H.: Analysis of peptides of the moderately lysine rich histone fraction, F 2B, of the Walker tumor and other tissues. *Exp. Cell. Res., Suppl. 9:*367, 1963.

HOAGLAND, M. B., SCORNIK, O. A., and PFEFFERKORN, L. C.: Aspects of control of protein synthesis in normal and regenerating rat liver, II. A microsomal inhibitor of amino acid incorporation whose action is antagonized by guanosine triphosphate. *Proc. Nat. Acad. Sci., 51:*1184, 1964.

HOLLAND, J. J.: Effects of puromycin on RNA synthesis in mammalian cells. *Proc. Nat. Acad. Sci., 50:*436, 1963.

HOLLEY, R. W., APGAR, J., EVERETT, G. A., MADISON, J. T., MARQUISSE, M., MERRILL, S. H., PENSWICK, J. R., and ZAMIR, A.: Structure of a ribonucleic acid. *Science, 147:*1462, 1965.

HOLMES, J. E., and ADEY, W. R.: Electrical activity of the entorhinal cortex during conditioned behavior. *Amer. J. Physiol., 199:*741, 1960.

HSIA, D. Y.: *Inborn Errors of Metabolism.* Chicago, Year Book Publishers, 1959.

HUDSPETH, W. J.: Strychnine: its facilitating effect on the solution of a simple oddity problem by the rat. *Science, 145:*1331, 1964.

HUDSPETH, W. J., and GERBRANDT, L. K.: Electroconvulsive shock: conflict, competition, consolidation, neuroanatomical considerations. *Psychol. Bull., 63:*377, 1965.

HUDSPETH, W. J., McGAUGH, J. L., and THOMSON, C. W.: Aversive and amnesic effects of electroconvulsive shocks. *J. Comp. Physiol. Psychol., 57*:61, 1964.

HUANG, R. C., and BONNER, J.: Histone, a suppressor of chromosomal RNA synthesis. *Proc. Nat. Acad. Sci., 48*:1216, 1962.

HURWITZ, J., and AUGUST, J. T.: The role of DNA in RNA synthesis. In J. N. Davidson and W. E. Cohn (Eds.), *Progress in Nucleic Acid Research*. New York, Academic Press, 1963.

HURWITZ, J., and FURTH, J. J.: Messenger RNA. *Sci. Amer., 206*:41, 1962.

HYDÉN, H.: Biochemical changes in glial cells and nerve cells at varying activity. In *Proc. 4th Intern. Congr. Biochem. Biochemistry of the Central Nervous System, Vol. III*. London, Pergamon Press, 1959.

HYDÉN, H.: Satellite cells in the nervous system. *Sci. Amer., 205*:62, 1961.

HYDÉN, H.: The neuron and its glia—a biochemical and functional unit. *Endeavor, 21*:144, 1962.

HYDÉN, H.: Biochemical and functional interplay between neuron and glia. In J. Wortis (Ed.), *Recent Advances in Biological Psychiatry, Vol. VI*. New York, Plenum Press, 1964.

HYDÉN, H., and EGHAZI, E.: Nuclear RNA changes of nerve cells during a learning experiment in rats. *Proc. Nat. Acad. Sci., 48*:1366, 1962.

HYDÉN, H., and EGYHAZI, E.: Glial RNA changes during a learning experiment with rats. *Proc. Nat. Acad. Sci., 49*:618, 1963.

HYDÉN, H., and EGYHAZI, E.: Changes in RNA content and base composition in cortical neurons of rates in a learning experiment involving transfer of handedness. *Proc. Nat. Acad. Sci., 52*:1030, 1964.

HYDÉN, H., and LANGE, P.: Difference in the metabolism of oligodendroglia and nerve cells in the vestibular area. In *4th International Neurochemical Symposium*. New York, Pergamon Press, 1960.

IYER, V. N., and SZYBALSKI, W.: Mitomycins and porfiromycin: chemical mechanism of activation and crosslinking of DNA. *Science, 145*:55, 1964.

IZAWA, M., ALLFREY, V. G., and MIRSKY, A. E.: The relationship between RNA synthesis and loop structure in lampbrush chromosomes. *Proc. Nat. Acad. Sci., 49*:544, 1963.

JACOB, F., and MONOD, J.: Genetic regulatory mechanisms in the synthesis of proteins. *J. Molec. Biol., 3*:318, 1961.

JACOBSEN, A. L., BABICH, F. R., BUBASH, S., and GOREN, C.: Maze preference in naive rats produced by injection of ribonucleic acid from trained rats. *Psychon. Sci., 4:3,* 1966.

JASPER, H. H.: Functional properties of the thalamic reticular system. In J. F. Delayfresnaye (Ed.), *Brain Mechanisms and Consciousness.* Oxford, Blackwell, 1956.

JASPER, H. H.: Recent advances in our understanding of ascending activities of the reticular system. In H. H. Jasper, L. D. Proctor, R. S. Knighton, W. C. Noshay, and R. T. Costello (Eds.), *Reticular Formation of the Brain.* Boston, Little, Brown, 1958.

JASPER, H. H.: Unspecific thalamocortical relations. In J. Field (Ed.), *Handbook of Physiology-Neurophysiology, Vol. II.* Baltimore, Williams and Wilkins, 1960.

JASPER, H. H., KHAN, R. T., and ELLIOTT, K. A. C.: Amino acids released from the cerebral cortex in relation to its state of activation. *Science, 147:*1448, 1965.

JEFFRESS, L. A. (Ed.): *Cerebral Mechanisms in Behavior.* New York, Wiley, 1951.

JOHN, E. R.: High nervous functions: brain functions and learning. In V. E. Hall, F. A. Fuhrman, and A. C. Giese (Eds.), *Annual Review of Physiology.* Palo Alto, Calif., Annual Reviews, 1961.

JOHN, E. R.: Studies on learning and retention in planaria. In M. A. B. Brazier (Ed.), *Brain Function. Vol. II. RNA and Brain Function—Memory and Learning.* Los Angeles, Univ. of Calif. Press, 1964.

JUKES, T. H.: Observations on the possible nature of the genetic code. *Biochem. Biophys. Res. Comm., 10:*155, 1963.

KALLMAN, F. J.: Genetic aspects of psychoses. In S. Cobb (Ed.), *The Biology of Mental Health and Disease.* New York, Hoeber, 1952.

KANAI, T., and SZERB, J. C.: Mesencephalic reticular activating system and cortical acetylcholine output. *Nature, 205:*80, 1965.

KARLSON, P.: Chemical and immunological aspects of hormones on the chemistry and mode of action of insect hormones. *Gen. Comp. Endocr., 1:*1, 1962.

KATZ, J. J., and HALSTEAD, W. C.: Protein organization and mental function. *Comp. Psychol. Monogr., 20:*103, 1950.

KAVANAU, J. L.: *Structure and Function in Biological Membranes. Vols. I and II.* San Francisco, Holden-Day, 1965.

KENNEY, F. T., and KULL, F. J.: Hydrocortisone-stimulated synthesis of nuclear RNA in enzyme induction. *Proc. Nat. Acad. Sci., 50:*493, 1963.

KILLAM, K. F.: Possible role of gamma-aminobutyric acid as an inhibitory transmitter. *Fed. Proc., 17:*1018, 1958.

KIMBLE, D. P.: The effects of bilateral hippocampal lesions in rats. *J. Comp. Physiol. Psychol., 56:*273, 1963.

KIMBLE, D. P., and PRIBRAM, K. H.: Hippocampectomy and behavior sequences. *Science, 139:*824, 1963.

KIRBY, R. S.: A new method for the isolation of ribonucleic acids from mammalian tissues. *Biochem. J., 64:*405, 1956.

KIRBY, R. S.: A new method for the isolation of deoxyribonucleic acids: evidence on the nature of bonds between deoxyribonucleic acid and protein. *Biochem. J., 66:*495, 1958.

KIT, S.: Equilibrium sedimentation in density gradients of DNA preparations from animal tissues. *J. Molec. Biol., 3:*711, 1961.

KJELGAARD, N. O., and KURLAND, C. G.: The distribution of soluble and ribosomal RNA as a function of growth rate. *J. Molec. Biol., 6:*341, 1963.

KLEITMAN, N.: Patterns of dreaming. *Sci. Amer., 203:*82, 1960.

KLOPFER, P. H.: Imprinting: a reassessment. *Science, 147:*302, 1965.

KOENIG, H.: Uptake of adenine—8 C^{14} and orotic—6—C^{14} acid into nuclear DNA of non-dividing cells in the adult feline neuraxis. *J. Biophys. Biochem. Cytology, 4:*664, 1958.

KOGAN, A. B.: Electrical activity and RNA of brain cells. In M. A. B. Brazier (Ed.) , *Brain Function. Vol. II. RNA and Brain Function—Memory and Learning.* Los Angeles, Univ. of Calif. Press, 1964.

KOHLER, W., and HELD, R.: The cortical correlates of pattern vision. *Science, 110:*414, 1949.

KONORSKI, J.: *Conditioned Reflexes and Neuron Organization.* Cambridge, Cambridge University Press, 1948.

KORNBERG, A.: *Enzymatic Synthesis of DNA.* New York, Wiley, 1961.

KRAL, V. A., and SVED, S.: Clinical and biochemical remarks on the ribonucleic acid treatment of Alzheimer's disease. Paper presented in symposium entitled *Nucleic Acids and Behavior,* Midwestern Psychological Association meetings, Chicago, Illinois, May 2, 1963.

KRECH, D., ROSENZWEIG, M. R., and BENNETT, E. L.: Dimensions of discrimination and level of cholinesterase activity in the cerebral cortex of the rat. *J. Comp. Physiol. Psychol., 49:*261, 1956.

KRECH, D., ROSENZWEIG, M. R., and BENNETT, E. L.: Correlation between brain cholinesterase and brain weight within two strains of rats. *Amer. J. Physiol., 196:*31, 1959.

KRECH, D., ROSENZWEIG, M. R., BENNETT, E. L., and KRUECKEL, B.:

Enzyme concentration in the brain and adjustive behavior patterns. *Science, 120:*994, 1954.

KRECH, D., ROSENZWEIG, M. R., BENNETT, E. L., and LONGUEIL, C. L.: Changes in brain chemistry of the rat following experience. Paper read at American Psychological Association, Cincinnati, 1959.

KURNICK, N. B., and NOKAY, N.: Changes induced in the mouse spleen by graded doses of total body x-irradiation. *Radiat. Res., 17:*140, 1963.

LANDAUER, T. K.: Two hypotheses concerning the biochemical basis of memory. *Psychol. Rev., 71:*167, 1964.

LANGRIDGE, R.: Ribosomes: a common structural feature. *Science, 140:* 1000, 1963.

LANGRIDGE, R., and GOMATOS, P. J.: The structure of RNA. *Science, 141:*694, 1963.

LASHLEY, K. S.: *Brain Mechanisms and Intelligence.* Chicago, Univ. of Chicago Press, 1929.

LEBARON, F. N.: Neurochemistry. In J. M. Luck, F. W. Allen, and G. Mackinney (Eds.), *Annual Review of Biochemistry.* Palo Alto, Annual Reviews, 1959.

LEONARD, D. J., and ZAVALA, A.: Electroconvulsive shock: retroactive amnesia and the single-shock method. *Science, 146:*1073, 1964.

LESLIE, I.: The nucleic acid content of tissues and cells. In E. Chargaff and J. N. Davidson (Eds.), *The Nucleic Acids, Vol. II.* New York, Academic Press, 1955.

LEWIS, D. J., and MAHER, B. A.: Neural consolidation and electroconvulsive shock. *Psychol. Rev., 72:*225, 1965.

LINDSLEY, D. B.: The reticular system and perceptual discrimination. In H. H. Jasper, L. D. Proctor, R. S. Knighton, W. C. Noshay, and R. T. Costello (Eds.), *Reticular Formation of the Brain.* Boston, Little, Brown, 1958.

LINDSLEY, D. B.: Attention, consciousness, sleep and wakefulness. In J. Field, H. W. Magoun, and V. E. Hall (Eds.), *Handbook of Physiology—Neurophysiology, Vol. III.* Baltimore, Williams and Wilkins, 1960.

LITTAU, V. C., ALLFREY, V. G., FRENSTER, J. H., and MIRSKY, A. E.: Active and inactive regions of nuclear chromatin as revealed by electron microscope autoradiography. *Proc. Nat. Acad. Sci., 52:* 93, 1964.

LIVINGSTON, R. B.: Central control of afferent activity. In H. H. Jasper, L. D. Proctor, R. S. Knighton, W. C. Noshay, and R. T. Costello (Eds.), *Reticular Formation of the Brain.* Boston, Little, Brown, 1958.

LIVINGSTON, R. B.: Central control of receptors and sensory transmission systems. In J. Field (Ed.), *Handbook of Physiology—Neurophysiology, Vol. I.* Baltimore, Williams and Wilkins, 1959.

LOEWY, A. G., and SIEKEVITZ, P.: *Cell Structure and Function.* New York, Holt, 1963.

LUTTGES, M., JOHNSON, T., BUCK, C., HOLLAND, J., and McGAUGH, J.: An examination of "transfer of learning" by nucleic acid. *Science, 151:*834, 1966.

LUZZATI, V.: The structure of DNA as determined by x-ray scattering techniques. In J. N. Davidson and W. E. Cohn (Eds.), *Progress In Nucleic Acid Research, Vol. I.* New York, Academic Press, 1963.

MADSEN, M. C., and McGAUGH, J. L.: The effect of ECS on one-trial avoidance learning. *J. Comp. Physiol. Psychol., 54:*522, 1961.

MACLEAN, P. D.: Psychosomatics. In J. Field (Ed.), *Handbook of Physiology—Neurophysiology, Vol. III.* Baltimore, Williams and Wilkins, 1960.

MAGOUN, H.: The ascending reticular system and wakefulness. In J. F. Delayfresnaye (Ed.), *Brain Mechanisms and Consciousness.* Oxford, Blackwell, 1956.

MAGOUN, H. W.: *The Waking Brain.* Springfield, Thomas, 1963.

MANDEL, P., and HARTH, S.: Free nucleotides of the brain in various mammals. *J. Neurochem., 8:*116, 1961.

MANDEL, P., HARTH, S., and BORKOWSKI, T.: Metabolism of the nucleic acids in various zones of the brain. In S. S. Kety and J. Elkes (Eds.), *Regional Neurochemistry.* New York, Pergamon Press, 1961.

MANDEL, P., BORKOWSKI, T., HARTH, S., and MARDELL, R.: Incorporation of ^{32}P in ribonucleic acid of subcellular fractions of various regions of the rat central nervous system. *J. Neurochem., 8:*126, 1961.

MARKERT, C. L.: Developmental genetics. In *The Harvey Lectures, Series 59.* New York, Academic Press, 1965.

MARMUR, J., and DOTY, P.: Determination of the base composition of deoxyribonucleic acid from its thermal denaturation temperature. *J. Molec. Biol., 5:*109, 1962.

MASON, J. W.: The central nervous system regulation of ACTH secretion. In H. H. Jasper, L. P. Proctor, R. S. Knighton, W. C. Noshay, and R. T. Costello (Eds.), *Reticular Formation of the Brain.* Boston, Little, Brown, 1958.

MATTHAEI, J. H., JONES, O. W., MARTIN, R. G., and NIRENBERG, M. W.: Characteristics and composition of RNA coding units. *Proc. Nat. Acad. Sci., 48:*666, 1962.

McCarthy, B. J., and Bolton, E. J.: An approach to the measurement of genetic relatedness among organisms. *Proc. Nat. Acad. Sci., 50:* 156, 1963.

McConnell, J. V.: RNA and memory. Paper presented in *Symposium on the Role of Macromolecules in Complex Behavior,* Kansas State University, Manhattan, 1964.

McGaugh, J. L., Jennings, R. D., and Thomson, C. W.: Effect of distribution of practice on the maze of learning of descendants of the Tyron maze bright and maze dull strains. *Psychol. Rep., 10:*147, 1962.

McGaugh, J. L., and Madsen, M. C.: Amnesic and punishing effects of electroconvulsive shock. *Science, 144:*182, 1964.

McGaugh, J. L., Westbrook, W. H., and Burt, G. S.: Strain differences in the facilitative effects of 5-7 diphenyl-l-3-diazadamantan-6-01 (1757 I.S.) on maze learning. *J. Comp. Physiol. Psychol., 54:* 502, 1961.

Meselson, M., and Stahl, F. W.: The replication of DNA in *Escherichia coli. Proc. Nat. Acad. Sci., 44:*671, 1958.

Mihailovic, L., Jankovic, B. D., Petkovic, M., and Isakovic, K.: Effect of electroshock upon nucleic acid concentrations in various parts of the cat brain. *Experientia, 14:*144, 1958.

Miller, G. A.: What is information measurement? *Amer. Psychol., 8:*3, 1953.

Miller, N. E.: Chemical coding of behavior in the brain. *Science, 148:* 328, 1965.

Milner, P. M.: The cell assembly: Mark II. *Psychol. Rev., 64:*242, 1957.

Mitchell, J. F.: The spontaneous and evoked release of acetylcholine from the cerebral cortex. *J. Physiol., 165:*98, 1963.

Morgan, C. T.: *Physiological Psychology.* New York, McGraw-Hill, 1965.

Morgan, C. T., and Stellar, E.: *Physiological Psychology.* New York, McGraw-Hill, 1950.

Morrell, F.: Electrophysiological contributions to the neural basis of learning. *Physiol. Rev., 41:*442-494, 1961.

Neidle, A., and Waelsch, H.: Histones: species and tissue specificity. *Science, 145:*1059, 1964.

Nielson, J. M.: *Agnosia, Apraxia, Aphasia: their Values in Cerebral Localization.* New York, Hoeber, 1946.

Nirenberg, M. W.: The genetic code: II. *Sci. Amer., 208:*80, 1963.

Nirenberg, M. W.: Nucleic acids in relation to the coding of genetic information. In M.A.B. Brazier (Ed.), *Brain Function. Vol. II. RNA and Brain Function—Memory and Learning.* Los Angeles, Univ. of Calif. Press, 1964.

NOACH, E. L., BUNK, J. J., and WIJLING, A.: Influence of electroshock and phenobarbital on nucleic acid content of rat brain cortex. *Acta Physiol. Pharmacol. Neerl., 11:*54, 1962.

O'BRIEN, J. S.: Stability of the myelin membrane. *Science, 147:*1099, 1965.

OCHOA, S.: Enzymatic mechanisms in the transmission of genetic information. In M. Kasha and B. Pullman (Eds.), *Horizons in Biochemistry.* New York, Academic Press, 1962.

OCHS, S.: Elements of Neurophysiology. New York, Wiley, 1965.

OCHS, S.: Axoplasmic flow in neurons. In J. Gaito (Ed.), *Macromolecules and Behavior.* New York, Appleton-Century-Crofts, 1966.

OKTAKA, Y., and SPIEGELMAN, S.: Translational control of protein synthesis in a cell-free system directed by a polycistornic viral RNA. *Science, 142:*493, 1963.

OLDS, J.: A preliminary mapping of electrical reinforcing effects in the rat brain. *J. Comp. Physiol. Psychol., 49:*507, 1956.

OLSON, R. E.: Vitamin K induced prothrombin formation: antagonism by actinomycin D. *Science, 145:*926, 1964.

OLSZEWSKI, J.: The cytoarchitechture of the human reticular formation. In J. F. Delayfresnaye (Ed.), *Brain Mechanisms and Consciousness.* Oxford, Blackwell, 1956.

OVERALL, J. E.: A cognitive probability model for learning. *Psychometrika, 25:*159, 1960.

PAGE, J. H.: Thudichum and the chemistry of the brain. In K.A.C. Elliot, I. H. Page, and J. H. Quastel (Eds.), *Neurochemistry.* Springfield, Thomas, 1955.

PAINTER, T. S.: Fundamental chromosome structure. *Proc. Nat. Acad. Sci., 51:*1282, 1964.

PALLADIN, A. V., and Vladimirov, G. E.: The use of radioactive isotopes in the study of the functional biochemistry of the brain. *In Proceedings of the International Conference on the Peaceful Uses of the Atomic Energy, Vol. XII.* New York, United Nations, 1956.

PARDEE, A. B.: Aspects of genetic and metabolic control of protein synthesis. In J. M. Allen (Ed.), *The Molecular Control of Cellular Activity.* New York, McGraw-Hill, 1962.

PEARLMAN, C. A., Jr.: Some aspects of localization of the consolidation process. Paper presented at the American Psychological Association Meetings, September 1963.

PEARLMAN, C. A., JR., SHARPLESS, S. K., and JARVIK, M. E.: Retrograde amnesia produced by anesthetic and convulsant agents. *J. Comp. Physiol. Psychol., 54*:109, 1961.

PENFIELD, W.: Studies of the cerebral cortex of man—a review and an interpretation. In J. F. Delayfresnaye (Ed.), *Brain Mechanisms and Consciousness.* Oxford, Blackwell, 1956.

PENFIELD, W.: The dawn of medicine. In H. H. Jasper, L. D. Proctor, R. S. Knighton, W. C. Noshay, and R. T. Costello (Eds.), *Reticular Formation of the Brain.* Boston, Little, Brown, 1958.

PENFIELD, W.: Neurophysiological basis of the higher functions of the nervous system—introduction. In J. Field (Ed.), *Handbook of Physiology-Neurophysiology, Vol. III.* Baltimore, Williams and Wilkins, 1960.

PENROSE, L. S.: Inborn errors of metabolism in relation to mental pathology. In K.A.C. Elliott, I. H. Page, and J. H. Quastel (Eds.), *Neurochemistry.* Springfield, Thomas, 1955.

PERRY, R. P., SRINIVASAN, P. R., and KELLEY, D. E.: Hybridization of rapidly labeled nuclear ribonucleic acids. *Science, 145*:504, 1964.

PEPEW, G., and MANTEGAZZINI, P.: Midbrain hemisection: effect on cortical acetylcholine in the cat. *Science, 145*:1069, 1964.

PEVZNER, L. Z.: Nucleic acid changes during behavioral events. In J. Gaito (Ed.), *Macromolecules and Behavior.* New York, Appleton-Century-Crofts, 1966.

PLATT, J. R.: A "book model" of genetic information transfer in cells and tissues. In M. Kasha and B. Pullman (Eds.), *Horizons in Biochemistry.* New York, Academic Press, 1962.

POLLARD, E. C.: Ionizing radiation: effect on genetic transcription. *Science, 146*:927, 1964.

POTTER, V. R.: *Nucleic Acid Outlines, Vol. I, Structure and Metabolism.* Minneapolis, Burgess, 1960.

PRIBRAM, K. H.: A review of theory in physiological psychology. In P. R. Farnsworth and Q. McNemar (Eds.), *Annual Review of Psychology.* Palo Alto, Annual Reviews, 1960.

PRIBRAM, K. H.: Reinforcement revisited: a structural view. In M. R. Jones (Ed.), *Nebraska Symposium on Motivation—1963.* Lincoln, Univ. Nebr. Press, 1963. (a)

PRIBRAM, K.: The new neurology: memory, novelty, thought, and choice. In G. H. Glaser (Ed.), *EEG and Behaviour.* New York, Basic Books, 1963. (b)

PRIBRAM, K.: Some notes on the structure of memory. Paper presented during *Symposium on the Role of Macromolecules in Complex Behaviour*, Kansas State University, April, 1964.

QUASTEL, J. H.: Acetylcholine distribution and synthesis in the central nervous system. In K. A. C. Elliott, J. H. Page, and J. H. Quastel (Eds.), *Neurochemistry*. Springfield, Thomas, 1962.

RAMEY, E. R., and O'DOHERTY, D. S. (Eds.) : *Electrical Studies of the Unanesthetized Brain*. New York, Hoeber, 1960.

RAY, O. S., and EMLEY, G.: Interhemispheric transfer of learning. *Life Sciences, 4:*271, 1965.

RAY, O. S., and EMLEY, G.: Time factors in interhemispheric transfer of learning. *Science, 144:*76, 1964.

REID, B. R., *and* COLE, R. D.: Biosynthesis of a lysine-rich histone in isolated calf thymus nuclei. *Proc. Nat. Acad. Sci., 51:*1044, 1964.

RESTLE, F. A.: A theory of discrimination learning. *Psychol. Rev., 62:* 11, 1955.

RICH, A.: On the problems of evolution and biochemical information transfer. In M. Kasha and B. Pullman (Eds.), *Horizons in Biochemistry*. New York, Academic Press, 1962.

RINKEL, M., and DENBER, H. C. B. (Eds.) : *Chemical Concepts of Psychosis*. New York, McDowell, Obolensky, 1958.

RIS, H.: Chromosome structure. In W. D. McElroy and B. Glass (Eds.), *The Chemical Basis of Heredity*. Baltimore, The John Hopkins Press, 1957.

RIS, H.: The structure of nucleohistones in chromosomes. *Science, 146:*428, 1964.

ROBERTS, R. B.: Further implications of the doublet code. *Proc. Nat. Acad. Sci., 48:*1245, 1962.

ROBERTS, R. B., McQUILLEN, K., and ROBERTS, I. Z.: Biosynthetic aspects of metabolism. In C. E. Clifton, S. Roffel, and M. P. Starr (Eds.), *Annual Review of Microbiology, Vol. XIII*. Palo Alto, Annual Reviews, 1959.

ROBINSON, A., and PUCK, T. T.: Sex chromatin in newborns: presumptive evidence for external factors in human nondisjunction. *Science, 148:*83, 1965.

ROSENBLATT, F.: The perceptron: a probabilistic model for information storage and organization in the brain. *Psychol. Rev., 65:*386, 1958.

ROSENZWEIG, M. R.: Effects of heredity and environment on brain chemistry, brain anatomy, and learning ability in the rat. In A. J. Edwards and J. J. Cowley (Eds.), *Physiological Determinates of*

Behaviour: Implications for Mental Retardation. Lawrence, Univ. Kansas Press, 1964.

ROSENZWEIG, M. R., KRECH, D., and BENNETT, E. L.: Effects of pentobarbital sodium on adaptive behaviour patterns in the rat. *Science, 123:*371, 1956.

ROSENZWEIG, M. R., KRECH, D., and BENNETT, E. L.: A search for relations between brain chemistry and behaviour. *Psychol. Bull., 57:* 476, 1960.

ROUNDS, D. E., and SLICK, W. C.: A correlative study of RNA content and the degree of radioresistance of cells *in vitro.* Technical Documentary Report No. SAM-TDR-63-17, USAF School of Aerospace Medicine, Brooks Air Force Base, Texas, 1963.

RUBIN, L. S.: Recent advances in the chemistry of psychotic disorders. *Psychol. Bull., 56:*375, 1959.

RUBIN, L. S.: Patterns of adrenergic-cholinergeic imbalance in the functional psychoses. *Psychol. Rev., 69:*301, 1962.

RUSSELL, R. W.: Psychopharmacology. In P. R. Farnsworth, O. Mcnemar, and Q. McNemar (Eds.), *Annual Review of Psychology.* Palo Alto, Annual reviews, 1964.

SABESIN, S. M., and ISSELBACHER, K. J.: Protein synthesis inhibition: mechanism for the production of impaired fat absorption. *Science, 147:*1149, 1965.

SAGER, R., and RYAN, F. J.: *Cell Heredity.* New York, Wiley, 1961.

SALMIRAGHI, G. C., and BLOOM, F. E.: Pharmacology of individual neurons. *Science, 144:*493, 1964.

SAMPSON, M., KATOH, A., HOTTA, Y., and STERN, H.: Metabolically labile deoxyribonucleic acid. *Proc. Nat. Acad. Sci., 50:*459, 1963.

SANTEN, R. J., and AGRANOFF, B. W.: Studies on the estimation of deoxyribonucleic acid and ribonucleic acid in rat brain. *Biochim. Biophys. Acta, 72:*251, 1963.

SANTER, M.: Ribosomal RNA on the surface of ribosomes. *Science, 141:*1049, 1962.

SCHADE, J. P., and PASCOE, E. G.: Maturational changes in cerebral cortex III. Effects of methionine sulfoxime on some electrical parameters and dendritic organization of cortical neurons. In W. A. Himwich and H. E. Himwich (Eds.), *The Developing Brain.* New York, Elsevier, 1964.

SCHADE, J. P., VAN BACKER, H., and SOLON, E.: Quantitative analysis of neuronal parameters in the maturing cerebral cortex. In D. P. Purpura and J. P. Schade (Eds.), *Growth and Maturation of the Brain.* New York, Elsevier, 1964.

SCHILDKRAUT, C. L., MARMUR, J., and DOTY, P.: Determination of the base composition of deoxyribonucleic acid from its buoyant density in CsCl. *J. Molec. Biol., 4:*430, 1962.

SCHMIDT, G., and THANNHEUSER, S. J.: A method for the determination of deoxyribonucleic acid, ribonuclenic acid, and phosphoproteins in animal tissues. *J. Biol. Chem., 161:*83, 1945.

SCHMITT, F. O. (Ed.), *Macromolecular Specificity and Biological Memory.* Cambridge, M.I.T. Press, 1962.

SCHNEIDERMAN, H. A., and GILBERT, L. J.: Control of growth and development in insects. *Science, 143:*325, 1964.

SCHWAB, R. S.: *Electroencephalography in Clinical Practice.* Philadelphia, Saunders, 1951.

SCOTT, R. B., and BELL, E.: Protein synthesis during development: control through messenger RNA. *Science, 145:*711, 1964.

SCOTT, R. B., and BELL, E.: Messenger RNA utilization during development of chick embryo lens. *Science, 147:*405, 1965.

SEHON, A.: Stereospecificity. *Science, 148:*401, 1965.

SELLS, B. H.: Puromycin: effect on messenger RNA synthesis and β-galactosidase formation in Eschericia coli 15T —. *Science, 148:* 371, 1965.

SHARPLESS, S. K.: Reorganization of function in the nervous system—use and disuse. In V. E. Hall, A. C. Giese, and R. R. Sonnenschein (Eds.), *Annual Review of Physiology.* Palo Alto, Annual Reviews, 1964.

SHUGAR, D.: Photochemistry of nucleic acids and their constituents. In E. Chargaff and J. N. Davidson (Eds.), *The Nucleic Acids, Vol. 3.* New York, Academic Press, 1960.

SIDRONSKY, H., STAEHELIN, T., and VERNEY, E.: Protein synthesis enhanced in the liver of rats force-fed a threonine-devoid diet. *Science, 146:*766, 1964.

SIMON, C. W.: Some immediate effects of drowsiness and sleep on normal human performance. *Human Factors,* March 1961, pp. 1-17.

SIMON, E. J., and VAN PRAGG, D.: Selective inhibition of synthesis of ribosomal RNA in Eschericia coli by levorphanol. *Proc. Nat. Acad. Sci., 51:*1151, 1964.

SINSHEIMER, R. L.: The biochemistry of genetic factors. In J. M. Luck, F. W. Allen, and G. Mackinney (Eds.), *Annual Review of Biochemistry.* Palo Alto, *Annual Reviews,* 1960.

SMELLIE, R. M. S.: The biosynthesis of ribonucleic acid in animal systems. In J. N. Davidson and W. E. Cohn (Eds.), *Progress in Nucleic Acid Research, Vol. I.* New York, Academic Press, 1963.

SMITH, C. E.: Is memory a matter of enzyme induction? *Science, 138:*

889, 1962.

SMITH, J. D.: The electrophoretic separation of nucleic acid components. In E. Chargaff and J. N. Davidson (Eds.), *The Nucleic Acids, Vol. I.* New York, Academic Press, 1955.

SOLOMON, P., Kubzansky, P. E., LEIDERMAN, P. H., MENDELSON, J. H., TRUMBULL, R., and WEXLER, D. (Eds.): *Sensory Deprivation.* Cambridge, Harvard Univ. Press, 1961.

SONNEBORN, T. M.: The differentiation of cells. *Proc. Nat. Acad. Sci., 51:*915, 1964.

SONNEBORN, T. M.: Nucleotide sequence of a gene: first complete specification. *Science, 148:*1410, 1965.

SPERRY, R. W.: The growth of nerve circuits. *Sci. Amer., 201:*68, 1959.

SPERRY, W. M.: The biochemistry of the brain during early development. In K. A. C. Elliott, J. H. Page, and J. H. Quastel (Eds.) *Neurochemistry.* Springfield, Thomas, 1962.

SPIEGELMAN, S.: Information transfer from the genome. *Fed. Proc., 22:* 36, 1963.

SPORN, M. B., and DINGMAN, C. W.: Histone and DNA in isolated nuclei from chicken brain, liver and erythrocytes. *Science, 140:* 316, 1963.

SPORN, M. B., WANKO, T., and DINGMAN, W.: The isolation of cell nuclei from rat brain. *J. Cell. Biol., 15:*109, 1962.

SRINIVASAN, P. R., and BOREK, E.: Enzymatic alteration of nucleic acid structure. *Science, 145:*548, 1964.

STAEHELIN, T., WETTSTEIN, F. O., and NOLL, H.: Breakdown of rat-liver ergosomes in vivo after actinomycin inhibition of messenger RNA synthesis. *Science, 140:*180, 1963.

STANLEY, W. M., and VALENS, E. G.: *Viruses and the Nature of Life.* New York, Dutton, 1961.

STEDMAN, E., and STEDMAN, E.: Cell specificity of histones. *Nature, 166:* 780, 1950.

STELLAR, E.: Drive and motivation. In J. Field (Ed.), *Handbook of Physiology-Neurophysiology, Vol. III.* Baltimore, Williams and Wilkins, 1960.

STRAUSS, B. S.: *An Outline of Chemical Genetics.* Philadelphia, Saunders, 1960.

SUEOKA, N.: Variation and heterogeneity of base composition of deoxyribonucleic acids: a compilation of old and new data. *J. Molec. Biol., 3:*31, 1961.

SUEOKA, N., and CHENG, T. Y.: Fractoination of nucleic acids with the methylated albumin column. *J. Molec. Biol., 4:*161, 1962.

SUZUKI, K., KOREY, S. R., and TERRY, R. D.: Studies on protein synthesis in brain microsomal system. *J. Neurochem., 11:*403, 1964.

SWIFT, H.: Nucleic acids and cell morphology in dipterian salivary glands. In J. M. Allen (Ed.), *The Molecular Control of Cellular Activity.* New York, McGraw-Hill, 1962.

SYPHERD, P. S., and STRAUSS, N.: The role of RNA in repression of enzyme synthesis. *Proc. Nat. Acad. Sci., 50:*1059, 1963.

SYTIVSKY, I. A., and THINH, N. T.: The distribution of γ-aminobutyric acid in the monkey brain during picrotoxin-induced seizures. *J. Neurochem., 11:*551, 1964.

TAKAHASHI, R., and APRISON, M. H.: Acetylcholine content of discrete areas of the brain obtained by a near-freezing method. *J. Neurochem., 11:*887, 1964.

TALWAR, G. P., CHOPRA, S. P., and GOEL, B. K.: Correlation of functional activity of brain with metabolic parameters: RNA and protein metabolism of occipital cortex in relation to its activation by light stimulus. *Sixth International Congress of Biochemistry,* 1964. (abstract)

TALWAR, G. P., GOEL, B. K., CHOPRA, S. P., and D'MONTE, B.: Brain RNA — some information on its nature and metabolism as revealed by studies during experimentally induced convulsions and in response to sensory stimulation. In J. Gaito (Ed.), *Macromolecules and Behavior.* New York, Appleton-Century-Crofts, 1966.

TALWAR, G. P., SADASIVUDU, B., and CHITRE, V. S.: Changes in pentose-nucleic acid content of sub-cellular fractions of the brain of the rat during Metrazol convulsions. *Nature, 191:*1007, 1961.

TATUM, E. L.: Medicine and molecular genetics. *Bull. N. Y. Acad. Sci., 40:*1, 1964.

TENEN, S. S.: Retrograde amnesia from electroconvulsive shock in a one-trial appetitive learning task. *Science, 148:*1248, 1965.

THOMAS, G. J.: Neurophysiology of learning. In P. R. Farnsworth, O. McNemar, and Q. McNemar (Eds.). *Annual Review of Psychology.* Palo Alto, Calif., Annual Reviews, 1962.

THOMPSON, R.: The effect of ECS on retention in young and adult rats. *J. Comp. Physiol. Psychol., 50:*644, 1958,

THOMPSON, R., and MCCONNELL, J. V.: Classical conditioning in the planarian, *Dugesia dorotocephala. J. Comp. Physiol. Psychol., 48:*65, 1955.

THOMPSON, R., and PENNINGTON, D. F.: Memory decrement produced by ECS as a function of the distribution of original learning. *J. Comp. Physiol. Psychol., 50:*401, 1957.

THUDICHUM, J. L. W.: *A Treatise on the Chemical Constitution of the Brain.* London, Baliere, Tindall, and Cox, 1884.

Tobias, J. M.: A chemically specified molecular mechanism underlying excitation in nerve: a hypothesis. *Nature, 203:*13, 1964.

Tower, D. B.: The neurochemical substrates of cerebral function and activity. In H. F. Harlow and C. N. Woolsey (Eds.), *Biological and Biochemical Bases of Behavior.* Madison, Univer. Wisconsin Press, 1958.

Tower, D. B.: Chemical architecture of the central nervous system. In J. Field (Ed.), *Handbook of Physiology—Neurophysiology, Vol. III.* Baltimore, Williams and Wilkins, 1960.

Tsugita, A., and Fraenkel-Conrat, H.: The amino acid composition and C-terminal sequence of a chemically evoked mutant of TMV. *Proc. Nat. Acad. Sci., 46:*636, 1960.

Ungar, G., and Navarro, C. O.: Transfer of habituation by material extracted from brain. *Nature, 207:*301, 1965.

Vendrely, R.: The deoxyribonucleic acid content of the nucleus. In E. Chargaff and J. N. Davidson (Eds.), *The Nucleic Acids, Vol. II.* New York, Academic Press, 1955.

Vladimirov, G. E., Baronov, M. N., Pevzner, L. Z., and Tsyn-Yan, W.: On differences in metabolism existing in some areas and layers of brain cortex. In S. S. Kety and J. Elkes (Eds.), *Regional Neurochemistry.* New York, Pergamon Press, 1961.

Waisman, H. A., and Harlow, H. F.: Experimental phenylketonuria in infant monkeys. *Science, 147:*685, 1965.

Warner, J. R., and Rich, A.: The number of soluble RNA molecules on reticulocyte polyribosomes. *Proc. Nat. Acad. Sci., 51:*1134, 1964.

Warner, J. R., Rich, A., and Hall, C. E.: Electron microscope studies of ribosomal clusters synthesizing hemoglobin. *Science, 138:*1399, 1962.

Watson, J. D.: Involvement of RNA in the synthesis of protein. *Science, 140:*17, 1963.

Wechsler, D.: *The Measurement of Intelligence.* Baltimore, Williams and Wilkins, 1944.

Wegener, W. S., and Romano, A. H.: Zinc stimulation of RNA and proteifn synthesis in *Rhizopus nigricans. Science, 142:*1669, 1963.

Weiss, P.: The concept of perpetual neuronal growth and proximodistal substance convection. In *4th International Neurochemical Symposium.* New York, Pergamon Press, 1960.

Weiss, W. P., and Sokoloff, L.: Reversal of thyroxine-induced hypermetabolism by puromycin. *Science, 140:*1324, 1963.

Wicks, W. D., and Kenney, F. T.: RNA synthesis in rat seminal vesicles: stimulation by testosterone. *Science, 144:*1346, 1964.

WIENER, N.: *Cybernetics.* New York, Wiley, 1948.

WILKINS, M. H. F.: Molecular configuration of nucleic acids. *Science, 140*:941, 1963.

WILLIAMS, R. J.: *Biochemical Individuality: the Basis for the Genetotrophic Concept.* New York, Wiley, 1956.

WOOL, I. G., and MUNRO, A. J.: An influence of insulin on the synthesis of a rapidly labeled RNA by isolated rat diaphragm. *Proc. Nat. Acad. Sci., 50*:918, 1963.

WOOLDRIDGE, D. E.: *The Machinery of the Brain.* New York, McGraw-Hill, 1963.

WOOLEY, D. W.: *The Biochemical Bases of Psychoses.* New York, Wiley, 1962.

WYERS, E. J.: The caudate-inhibitory system and consolidation of memory. Paper presented at American Psychological Association Meetings, September 1963.

YAMAGAMI, S., KAWAKITA, Y., and NAKA, S.: Base composition of RNA of the subcellular fractions from guinea pig brains. *J. Neurochem., 11*:899, 1964.

YANKOFSKY, S. A., and SPIEGELMAN, S.: Distinct cistrons for the two ribosomal RNA components. *Proc. Nat. Acad. Sci., 49*:538, 1963.

ZAMENHOF, S., BURSZTYN, H., RICH, K., and ZAMENHOF, P. J.: The determination of deoxyribonucleic acid and of cell numbers in brain. *J. Neurochem., 11*:505, 1964.

ZELMAN, A., KABAT, L., JACOBSON, R., and McCONNELL, J. V.: Transfer of training through injection of "conditioned" RNA into untrained planarians. *Worm Runner's Digest, 5*:No. 1, 14, 1963.

ZUBAY, G.: Molecular model for protein synthesis. *Science, 140*:1092, 1963.

ZUBAY, G.: Nucleohistone structure and function. In J. Bonner and P. Ts'O (Eds.), *The Nucleohistones.* San Francisco, Holden-Day, 1964.

ZUCKERMAN, M., and COHEN, N.: Sources of reports of visual and auditory sensations in perceptual-isolation experiments. *Psychol. Bull., 62*:1, 1964.

SECTION IV
APPENDICES

APPENDIX A
SOME IMPORTANT METHODOLOGIES

CELL FRACTIONATION

A BASIC PROCEDURE for molecular biological studies is that of cell fractionation using differential centrifugation involving low and high speed centrifuges. Cells are composed of a heterogeneous composite of material varying in weights. If one ruptures the cell membrane and places the contents in a test tube the particles would settle naturally at varying portions of the tube. However, if one were to rotate the tube at a fast speed the particles would reach an equilibrium level much faster because increased gravitational forces (g) would result. This is essentially what is done in fractionating cell components by differential centrifugation.

The tissue of interest is broken down by grinding in a homogenizer with a suitable chemical medium such as sucrose so that the cell membranes will be disrupted. A series of centrifugations at varying speeds (and thus varying "g" forces) allow the sedimenting and collecting of each of the major components of the cell.

The first sediment to be obtained would be that with nuclei. In the case of rat tissue homogenates in 0.25 Molar (M) sucrose the nuclei will sediment with centrifugation for ten minutes at about 600xg. Unfortunately, in most tissue the nuclear component would contain a number of contaminants, e.g., in rat brain tissue myelin, capillary fragments, mitochondria, microsomes and red blood cells. Impure nuclear fractions probably occur in almost all tissues of organisms with this simple procedure. Thus if one is interested in obtaining "pure" nuclei, a series of centrifugations with the nuclear sediment is necessary. Sporn, Wanko and Dingman (1962) have suggested such a procedure with rat brain tissue which gave good results. Mandel, Borkowski, Harth and Mardell (1961) have reported a similar procedure.

If the supernatant from the nuclear fraction is centrifuged at about 5000xg, the mitochondria are obtained in the sediment. At this speed there is contamination with microsomes and the contamination increases with higher speeds. Again a series of centrifugation with the sediment would be required for "pure" mitochondria.

The next fraction to be separated is the microsomal one. This consists of endoplasmic reticulum plus the attached ribosomes. The first will sediment from the mitochondrial supernatant at 60,000 xg for less than an hour while the ribosomal portion requires forces of 105,000xg for about sixty minutes. If increased time and speeds of centrifugation are used, contamination will occur because other components in the supernatant will sediment, e.g., transfer RNA.

The supernatant from the microsomal fraction contains transfer RNA and this can be recovered by various chemical means.

CHROMATOGRAPHY

The principle of chromatographic methods is to adsorb the material of interest on an insoluble material and then to differentially remove or elute them one at a time with suitable liquid solvents. If the adsorbent is in the form of a sheet it is called paper chromatography; if the adsorbent is packed in a column it is column chromatography.

In paper chromatography filter paper is usually the adsorbent. For example, one can take an RNA sample which has been hydrolyzed by hydrochloric acid (HCl) to give a mixture of the four bases: A, G, C and U. A drop of this solution is placed on one end of the filter paper and the paper is placed in a sealed glass compartment. The end of the paper nearest the drop of sample is placed into a trough at the top of the compartment which contains a mixture of methanol, concentrated HCl and water (solvent) and the paper is hung freely so as not to touch the sides of the chamber. The solvent will descend on the paper and the RNA bases will move with the solvent but at different rates. A simple analogy is that of different boats moving at varying speeds on a lake.

The above procedures is called "descending paper chromatography." "Ascending paper chromatography" involves the solvent and samples ascending the filter paper. Furthermore, the above is also referred to as "one dimensional chromatography." For better separation of the samples, two or three dimensional techniques may be used. For example, the separation by the above solvent would give the following order from the origin: G, A, C and U. If the paper were rotated 90 degrees and again placed in the chamber with a new solvent (isopropanol, ammonium hydroxide, and water), increased separation would be effected and the bases would retain the same order.

After this operation the paper is removed and sprayed with a chemical which will accentuate a spot corresponding to each of the bases. Or one can preclude spraying by drying the paper and observing the spots with an ultraviolet light because the bases of the nucleic acids absorb in the ultra violet range.

Since the rate of migration of each base is a characteristic constant for each solvent system, the identity of each base can be determined readily. Each of the samples can be eluted by dilute HCl and the amounts determined by spectrophotometry.

In column chromatography the samples in solution are allowed to percolate slowly down the adsorbent. The solutes (samples) will be adsorbed at specific portions in the column. Homogeneous samples will give a single zone on the column; heterogeneous ones will show a number of bands. The adsorbed material can be freed by an eluting solvent and the amount determined by spectrophotometry or other procedures.

An example of a column chromatography procedure is that developed by Sueoka and Cheng (1962). The column consisted of kieselguhr impregnated with methylated albumin. DNA and RNA samples were adsorbed in the column and eluted by passing through the column a series of saline solutions of increasing salt concentrations. The samples could be separated according to molecular sizes, condition, and composition. DNA's with greater G-C content were eluted at lower salt concentrations. Thermally denatured DNA was eluted at a lower salt concentration than was native DNA. The method separated transfer and ribosomal RNA and also the two components of ribosomal RNA (16S and 23S).

ELECTROPHORESIS

A technique in some respects similar to paper chromatography is electrophoresis. Electrophoretic apparatus requires that the sample particles must be electrically active, i.e., ionized, and that the solution conduct electricity. Thus RNA could be hydrolyzed to the base components and a drop of the sample placed on filter paper or cellulose acetate paper in a suitable solution, e.g., citrate buffer. Each of the nucleic acid bases would migrate under electrical current at characteristic rates on the paper. For example, in an acid solution the amino groups of G, A and C are cationic, i.e., they are positive and will move toward the cathode. The bases could be located by ultraviolet light and eluted and estimated spectrophotometrically.

Holger Hyden has developed an elegant microelectrophoretic device which he uses with RNA bases obtained from single cells (1961). The bases migrate on a microscopic cellulose thread.

RADIOGRAPHY

Isotopes consist of either stable or radioactive ones. An example of a stable isotope is H^2 (deuterium), the common hydrogen atom. Radioactive isotopes emit some type of radiation indicating that atomic disintegrations are occurring, e.g., H^3 (tritium). The main instrument for determination of radioactivity is the spectrometer. A common example in molecular biology today is the liquid scintillation spectrometer. Radioactive samples in solution are placed in the spectrometer which counts the number of atomic disintegrations that occur per second.

Radioactive substances are usually employed as a portion of molecules which the organisms is to utilize, e.g., H^3 in tritiated uridine which will be incorporated in RNA or tritiated thymidine for DNA. The substance is injected into the animal or placed in the medium. Such procedures allow one to determine the synthesis patterns and activity rates for various chemicals and the anatomical location wherein these events are occurring. For this last aspect autoradiography has been most useful. Photographic film is applied to a cut section of tissue, exposed, and developed.

The portions of the film close to radioactive areas of the tissue will show darkened spots or dark lines radiating from a focal point corresponding to paths of radiation. The resolution by this method depends on the range of the particles. The range of beta particles from H^3 is so small that silver granules are formed immediately over the point at which isotope decay occurs. Carbon-14 gives poor resolution because it emits beta particles with longer ranges, thus making a determination of the exact point of origin relatively uncertain. The autoradiographic procedure has been combined with electron microscopy to provide detailed analysis of intracellular activity (Hay and Revell, 1963).

SPECTROPHOTOMETRY

A spectrophotometer is a device for detecting light absorption or transmittance at various wave lengths. Because very narrow wave lengths are employed there is greater freedom from interfering compounds than is the case with a photometer. The nucleic acids show marked absorption in the ultraviolet regions of the electromagnetic spectrum with maximum near 260 millimicrons $(m\mu)$. Spectrophotometric analyses allow one to identify the nucleic acids and components and to determine the amounts of each of these.

Spectrophotometry is important in conjunction with other methods, e.g., thermal denaturation. It is a useful fact that when DNA is denatured into single strands the absorbance at 260 $m\mu$ increases. The absorbance of intact DNA or RNA is also less than the sum of the absorbances for each of the four components (Shugar, 1960).

SUBSTITUTION OF BASE ANALOGUES FOR USUAL BASES

A prominent procedure in assaying the function of the nucleic acids has been to substitute unusual bases for the normal ones. The purine and pyrimidine analogues are basically similar to the natural bases but differ in some small way.

Dunn and Smith (1954) have shown that in *E. coli* 5-bromo-uracil is incorporated into DNA and replaces T. They found that the addition of either 5-bromouracil or 5-iodouracil inhibited the natural reactions of *E. coli*. In these two cases the usual methyl group (CH_3) at the fifth carbon position is replaced by a bromine or iodine. Two to four hours after addition of the base analogues, the mean generation time of the bacteria was increased; the degree of inhibition increased with greater amounts of base analogues. However, inhibition could be reversed by T. After inhibition by either analogue, the proportion of bacteria giving colonies on nutrient agar was reduced. When all of the T was replaced by bromouracil, 9 per cent of the phage articles yielded viable progeny (Strauss, 1960).

5-bromouracil and 2-aminopurine are presumed to act to bring about the replacement of the A-T nucleotide pairs by G-C ones, and vice versa. These agents also bring about a reversion of these changes. 2-aminopurine is similar to G but has an H group rather than an OH group (hydroxyl) at carbon 2.

8-azaguanine is an analogue which has found some use in behavioral studies. It has a nitrogen at position 8 whereas a carbon is located there in G.

INHIBITION PROCEDURES

It has been common for researchers to utilize chemical agents which inhibit the functioning of the macromolecules (Hand-schumacher and Welch, 1960). For example, mitomycin or ethidium bromide inhibits DNA synthesis. Mitomycin is an anti-biotic with carcinostatic activity which has been shown to interfere with the synthesis of purine nucleotides in *E. coli* DNA without affecting RNA or protein synthesis. Recently Iyer and Szybalski (1964) have indicated that mitomycin in lethal concentrations crosslinks the complementary strands of DNA, the crosslinking being the basis for the lethal effect. The crosslinking reaction required at least two reactive sites on mitomycin before it was activated. The exact sites on the DNA molecule participating in the crosslinking reaction were not determined. Further information (Tatum, 1964) indicated that mitomycin causes a rapid deploymerization of DNA, leading to a rapid loss of biological activity.

Ethidium bromide causes an almost instantaneous suppression

of DNA without influencing protein and RNA synthesis for some time.

Antrycide and actinomycin inhibit RNA synthesis. The former is a pyrimidine derivative which inhibits RNA activity but has delayed effects on DNA synthesis. Actinomycin has an affinity for the G in DNA, thus binding DNA and preventing the synthesis of messenger RNA; this event completely inhibits the formation of protein with little effect on DNA synthesis. The antibiotic inhibits both DNA and RNA polymerases but has a greater effect on the latter. Concentrations of the drug which completely inhibited RNA polymerase activity inhibited DNA polymerase activity about 5 per cent (Hurwitz and August, 1963). Synthetic AT polymers and apurinic acid (DNA after removal of purines) do not bind actinomycin (Goldberg, Rabinowitz and Reich, 1962).

Actinomycin has been the most frequently used inhibitor of RNA synthesis. It inhibits equally all types of cellular RNA. A substance which has a selective inhibitory effect on ribosomal RNA is levorphanol. This structural analogue of morphine has been shown to inhibit ribosomal RNA synthesis by 90 to 95 per cent in *E. coli* whereas messenger and transfer RNA fractions continued synthesis at about half the usual rate (Simon and Van Praag, 1964).

Puromycin and chloramphenicol have been used to suppress protein synthesis. The former may inhibit synthesis of 30S and 18S ribosomal RNA and of larger ribosomal precursor RNA (Holland, 1963). However, in *E. coli* Sells (1965) reported that puromycin inhibited protein formation while allowing ribosomal and transfer RNA to accumulate. The synthesis of messenger RNA for β-galactosidase was not inhibited even though the synthesis of this enzyme was retarded. Thus it appears probable that puromycin inhibits protein synthesis at the ribosome; present views (Hector and Halkerston, 1965) indicate that it adds to messenger RNA in such a way that it terminates the sequence before the entire message is translated; fragmented sequences of amino acids are thereby released.

The RNA synthesized during chloramphenicol's presence is

reported to be abnormal in both physical properties and biological stability.

Colchicine prevents cell division without disturbing chromosome duplication. Thus one can observe the synthesis of DNA, RNA, and/or proteins unaffected by division events.

ENZYMATIC DEGRADATION AND HYDROLYTIC PROCEDURES

These procedures are of extreme importance in degrading the nucleic acids for many purposes. The pancreatic enzymes, RNase and DNase, attack the phosphate (P) ester linkages and are called phosphodiesterases. RNase attacks 3' pyrimidine P groups (P attached to carbon 3) with 5' OH groups of adjacent purines or pyrimidines. After RNase treatment for exhaustive digestion one obtains 3' uridylic acid, 3' cytidylic acid, and oligonucleotides consisting of two or more nucleotides. DNase action gives 5' mononucleotides but with fewer mononucleotides than is the case of RNase action on RNA. If all mononucleotides are desired, snake venom phosphodiesterase must be used following DNase and RNase treatment or on untreated RNA. The snake venom leaves products with 5' phosphate ends.

Acid or alkaline hydrolysis also will degrade the nucleic acids; however, DNA is the more resistant to hydrolytic agents and is not affected by alkaline agents because it is lacking an oxygen atom at the carbon 2 position. Treatment of RNA with 1 Normal (N) HCl at 100°C for one hour will free the purine bases, A and G, and the pyrimidines will be in mononucleotide form. Treatment with 88 per cent formic acid will free all bases. Treatment with 1 N potassium hydroxide (KOH) or sodium hydroxide (NaOH) at room temperature for one hour will result in mononucleotides of RNA. The first step involves a cyclical ester between the P and 2' and 3' OH groups which also occurs during RNase treatment. This step is impossible with DNA because only an H atom (rather than OH) is present at carbon 2.

If DNA is treated with 1 N HCl at 100°C for one hour the purines bases will be liberated but the pyrimidines will remain intact. If 70 per cent perchloric acid is used at 100°C for one hour the purine and pyrimidine bases will be removed but some pyrimidines will appear as nucleoside diphosphates (e.g., thymidylic acid plus an extra phosphate). Treatment with 88 per cent formic acid at 175°C for thirty minutes releases the four bases; this procedure is probably the most accurate of the DNA acid hydrolytic methods.

NEAREST NEIGHBOR ANALYSIS

An important problem in nucleic acid research is to determine the exact sequence of bases. Unfortunately, there are at present no simple reliable procedures for determining the overall base sequences. However, a simple and ingenious procedure provides information as to the sequence of two bases, the nearest neighbor analysis of Kornberg (1961). This procedure involves using radioactive phosphorus (P^{32}) which is attached to the fifth carbon of deoxyribose sugar. With a suitable environment and ingredients, DNA can be synthesized in the image of a DNA of interest to the experimenter. The DNA is then degraded by DNase and phosphodiesterase. This last step cleaves the P linkage at the carbon 5 bond. This results in the P^{32} being attached to the third carbon of the adjoining deoxyribose sugar. The overall procedure involves the P^{32} marker moving from one portion of the DNA to its neighbor. The base unit containing the P^{32} is then determined by chromatoghaphic and radiographic procedures. By labelling one of the DNA base units with P^{32} and repeating this procedure four times, each time with a different base unit being labelled, unit on which the P^{32} was attached originally. The other dimension gives the base unit in which the P^{32} is detected after degradation. One thus completes the table with the relative amounts of radioactivity. The overall result is the relative proportion of sequences of AA, AG, AC, AT, GA, GG, GC, GT, etc.

This procedure has been useful in indicating that even though two unrelated species have the same amounts of the bases in DNA, the sequences are different. This technique may be useful for behavioral studies eventually.

HYBRIDIZATION PROCEDURES

If DNA is heated to 90 to 100°C, the two strands will separate into single strands (denatured DNA). Upon slow cooling, reformation of double stranded DNA will occur. Such reformation occurs only between DNA strands which are from the same or related species (Spiegelman, 1963). The specificity requirement for a successful union of two strands indicates a need for a perfect or near-perfect complementarity in the nucleotides. The formation of a double stranded hybrid during slow cooling of a mixture of two kinds of polynucleotide strands has been accepted as evidence for complementarity in the sequence of bases in the two strands.

Not only is it possible for DNA-DNA hybrids to form, but DNA-RNA hybrids are possible as well and have been of great interest to scientists. If DNA is heated, rapidly cooled, and RNA is added to the solution, DNA-RNA hybrids will form. At portions of the hybrid containing large amounts of complementarity between the two strands a strong attachment will be produced. Other portions of the two-stranded molecule will form less strong attachments where only a portion of the base sequence of one is complementary to that of the other. This incomplete hybridization can be eliminated by adding RNase. The RNA at incomplete hybridization sites will be degraded but the RNA at complete hybridization loci will be resistant to the action of RNase.

Because DNA-RNA hybrids have a different density than either DNA or RNA molecules, the hybrids can be easily separated from the nucleic acids by equilibrium centrifugation in cesium chloride gradients. To insure more sensitive detection of DNA-RNA hybrids, the DNA can be labeled with H^3 and RNA with P^{32}, both radioactive materials. The two isotopes emit beta particles differing in their energies and can be assayed in each others presence in a scintillation spectrometer.

A different hybridization procedure has been developed by Bolton and McCarthy (1962). This involved heating DNA and then pouring it into agar; the DNA-agar components were cooled in an ice water bath to form a gel in which the DNA was trapped.

Labelled RNA or single stranded DNA is incubated at 60°C with the DNA-agar gel so as to form hybrids. The hybrids are recovered by washing with salt solutions. The authors used these procedures to measure the degree of genetic relatedness among organisms.

Recently Gillespie and Spiegelman (1965) have developed an improved and simplified hybridization method. Denatured DNA is immobilized on nitrocellulose membrane filters and complementary RNA is hybridized to the membrane fixed DNA. Unpaired RNA is removed by washing; RNase eliminates the RNA forming incomplete sequence bondings. The amounts of labelled RNA hybridizing with a known amount of labelled DNA are determined by analyzing the filters in a liquid scintillation spectrometer. This method allowed for increased sensitivity in identifying small regions of DNA complementary to a given RNA species; "noise" was reported to be depressed to a level of 0.003 per cent of the input RNA.

APPENDIX B

SOME EXTRACTION AND ANALYTIC PROCEDURES

THERE ARE NUMEROUS extraction and analytical procedures. Only a few of the more common ones will be discussed.

BIOLOGICALLY ACTIVE DNA

A number of procedures are available for extracting DNA, including the phenol, chloroform-isoamyl alcohol, and sodium lauryl sulfate procedures. These treatments involve rupturing the cells and performing a series of centrifugations with protein denaturants to separate the DNA from other materials. DNA is usually precipitated following each centrifugation and then mixed with the protein denaturant. Some RNA will be contaminating the DNA precipitate. After the proteins have been removed, RNase is added to eliminate RNA and then the RNase is removed with the protein denaturant. The treatments involve repeating the same procedure a number of times; the fewer the repetition steps the less pure will be the DNA extraction product; for "pure" DNA, ten to fifteen repetitions may be required.

The phenol procedure has been one of the most effective and widely used techniques. The various steps in extraction of DNA from small pieces of rat tissue with phenol will be outlined, a modification of the Kirby procedure (1958).

1) Mince tissue finely with scissors.

2) Grind the minced tissue with a motor driven pestle of the Potter-Elvejhem type in a solution of 0.30 M sodium-para-amino-salicylate.

3) Add 1 volume of 90 per cent phenol (weight by volume, w/v).

4) Shake for one hour.

5) Centrifuge at 1750 rpm for one hour at 0°C in an International Centrifuge.

240

6) The tube will appear as in Figure B-1 with DNA and some contaminants in the upper layer.

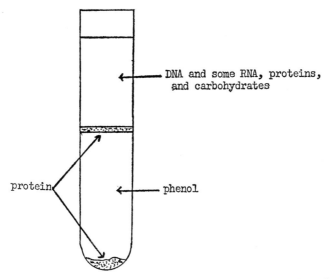

Figure B-1. The phases in the tube following the first centrifugation step.

7) Remove aqueous layer.

8) Wash remainder with the sodium-para-aminosalicylate solution and disperse the material.

9) Centrifuge at 1750 rpm for forty-five minutes.

10) Remove aqueous layer.

11) Repeat (8), (9) and (10) two more times.

12) Combine aqueous extracts.

13) Add one tenth the volume of 20 per cent potassium acetate to extracts to get 2 per cent solution.

14) Precipitate DNA with 2 volumes of ethanol.

15) The DNA precipitate is recovered by inserting a glass rod in the solution. The DNA will wind around the rod.

16) The precipitate is drained free of excess alcohol by gently pressing the rod against the side of the vessel.

17) The precipitate is placed in dilute saline citrate solution (0.015 M sodium chloride with 0.0015 M sodium citrate) and gently swirled back and forth until the DNA dissolves.

18) The solution is adjusted to approximately standard saline-citrate concentration (0.15 M sodium chloride with 0.015 M sodium citrate) by adding concentrated saline-citrate (1.5 M sodium chloride with 0.15 M sodium citrate).

19) Add 1 volume of 90 per cent phenol (w/v).

20) Shake for fifteen minutes.

21) Centrifuge at 1750 rpm for twenty minutes.

22) Repeat steps (7) through (21) a number of times until very little protein is seen at the interface.

23) The DNA in the aqueous layer obtained after the last in the series of deproteinizations is precipitated by adding 1/10 volume of 20 per cent potassium acetate and 2 volumes of ethanol.

24) The precipitate is dissolved as in steps (17) and (18), heated for ten minutes at 60°C, and RNase is added (50 μg/ml) and the mixture is incubated for thirty minutes at 37°C.

25) The protein RNase is removed by treating a number of times as in steps (19) through (23).

26) The final precipitate is washed free of acetate and salt by gently stirring it in progressively increasing solutions of ethanol (70 to 95 per cent) and dissolved in the solvent of choice.

The DNA extracted in this manner is biologically active and can be used for hybridization procedures and other treatments.

Variations of this procedure have been utilized. For example, some individuals introduce sodium lauryl sulfate prior to the phenol treatment for more effective results. The most effective procedure for a particular researcher working with a specific organism can be determined after trying a few variations of the basic phenol procedure.

BIOLOGICALLY ACTIVE RNA

Phenol has been effective also in isolating RNA. The procedure is similar to that in extracting DNA (Kirby, 1956).

1) Mince tissue.

2) Add 0.15 M sodium chloride (NaCl) and homogenize.

3) Add 1 volume of 90 per cent phenol (w/v).

4) Shake for one hour.

5) Centrifuge at 1750 rpm for 1 hour at 0°C in an International centrifuge.

6) The tube will appear as in Figure B-2.
7) Remove aqueous layer.
8) Wash remainder with 0.15 M NaCl.
9) Centrifuge at 1750 rpm for forty-five minutes.
10) Remove aqueous layer.

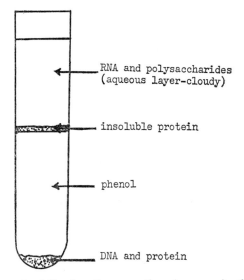

Figure B-2. The tube following first centrifugation step in the RNA extraction procedure.

11) Repeat (8), (9) and (10) two more times.
12) Combine aqueous extracts.
13) Add one tenth the volume of 20 per cent potassuim acetate to get 2 per cent solution.
14) Precipitate RNA with two volumes of ethanol.
15) Centrifuge at 1750 rpm for twenty minutes.
16) Wash precipitate with ethanol-water (3-1) several times until phenol smell is lost.
17) After each washing, centrifuge for twenty minutes at 1750 rpm.
18) Dissolve precipitate in 0.15 M NaCl.
19) Repeat steps (3) through (17) until the protein interface is very thin.

20) Dissolve the precipitate in 0.15 M NaCl and add DNase (50 μg/ml of solution) and incubate for thirty minutes at 37°C.

21) Add 1 volume of 90 per cent phenol and shake for fifteen minutes to eliminate DNase.

22) Centrifuge at 1750 rpm for twenty minutes at 0°C.

23) Repeat steps (7) through (17) a number of times.

24) The precipitate is dissolved in phosphate buffer and dialyzed against water to remove low molecular weight materials.

25) To the contents of the dialysis bag is added 1/10 volume of 20 per cent potassium acetate and two volumes of ethanol.

26) Centrifuge at 1750 rpm for twenty minutes.

27) Pour out fluid and evaporate remaining fluid from precipitate. This precipitate is RNA. It can be dissolved in solvent of choice.

The RNA extracted shows the properties of active RNA.

This extraction procedure has been illustrated in obtaining the RNA from the entire cell. However, it is applicable for obtaining the RNA from cell components also. For example to isolate ribosomal RNA, one would first separate the ribosomes in the manner indicated in Appendix A and proceed as above.

EXTRACTION OF BOTH NUCLEIC ACIDS

In many cases the researcher may desire to obtain both DNA and RNA, e.g., to dettrmine RNA/DNA ratios. The most prominent techniques to obtain both nucleic acids have arisen from the Schmidt-Thannhauser procedure (1945). In this case the nucleic acids are treated harshly (acid treatment) and biological activity may be lost. The procedure to be followed is that of Santen and Agranoff (1963) and involves separation of five fractions: lipids, low molecular weight materials, RNA nucleotides, DNA and protein.

1) Mince tissue.

2) Homogenize in chloroform-methanol solution (2:1, v/v) and transfer to centrifuge tube.

3) Rinse homogenizer with chloroform-methanol-water solution (38:19:3, v/v).

4) A Teflon coated stirring magnet is added to each tube to insure adequate extractions. Magnet is used in all remaining steps.

5) Centrifuge at 1000xg for ten minutes and draw off supernatant.

6) Residue is washed with chloroform-methanol-water solution, centrifuged for ten minutes and supernatant is obtained.

7) Residue is washed with chloroform-methanol-water solution one more time, centrifuged for ten minutes, and the supernatant is withdrawn and combined with the supernatant from steps (5) and (6) (lipid fraction).

8) Traces of chloroform are removed from residue by washing with 95 per cent ethanol to prevent formation of a gummy residue upon addition of trichloroacetic acid (TCA). Centrifuge for ten minutes and pour off supernatant.

9) Residue is washed two times with 5 per cent TCA (ice cold), centrifuged for ten minutes, and supernatants combined.

10) Residue is washed with cold 95 per cent ethanol, centrifuged for ten minutes, and supernatant is combined with those from steps (8) and (9) (low molecular weight materials).

11) Residue is washed with absolute ethanol, centrifuged for ten minutes, and supernatant discarded.

12) Step (11) is repeated with ether.

13) Residue is dried with a stream of nitrogen or by bubbling air into the tube.

14) Alkaline hydrolysis with 1 N KOH is performed at room temperature for one hour.

15) Tube with hydrolysate is placed in ice bath for one half hour.

16) 1/10 volume of 70 per cent perchloric acid (PCA) is added.

17) Residue is thoroughly resuspended by frequent mixing with Vortex Mixer for twenty minutes to insure complete separation of DNA and proteins.

18) Centrifuge for 10 minutes and draw off supernatant.

19) Residue is washed with cold 1 N PCA, centrifuged for 10 minutes, and supernatant added to that from step (18).

20) Repeat step (19) (RNA fraction).

21) Add 1 N PCA to residue and heat at 80°C for thirty minutes.

22) Centrifuge for ten minutes and withdraw supernatant.

23) Repeat steps (21) and (22) and combine supernatants (DNA fraction).

24) Dissolve residue in 1 N NaOH and let stand at room temperature overnight.

25) Resuspend material, centrifuge and draw off supernatant (protein fraction).

DETERMINATIONS OF AMOUNTS OF DNA AND RNA

Both nucleic acids absorb maximally at 260 mμ; thus the determination of amounts of each of these can be effected by spectrophotometric analyses at the wave length. However, if some contaminants are present which absorb around the same wavelength, a convenient method to use is a colorimetric one.

Orcinol Test (RNA)

The orcinol test is a standard and effective procedure for determining the amount of ribose by colorimetric means. A standard curve based on known amounts of ribose is obtained and then the value of the samples is estimated from the curve.

The RNA may be in hydrolyzed form as during the Santen-Agranoff procedure described above and be dissolved in 1 N PCA. The ribose for the standard curve should also be in 1 N PCA. The samples and standards should be brought to a volume of 1.5 milliliters (ml) with 1 N PCA. 3.0 ml of acid reagent (1.5 ml of hydrous ferric chloride — $FeCl_3.6\ H_2O$ — in 100 ml of concentrated HCl) is added and the tubes are shaken. 0.2 ml of purified 6 per cent orcinol in 95 per cent alcohol (made fresh daily) are added. Again the tubes are shaken and heated in a boiling water bath for twenty minutes. Varying shades of green will occur with the darkest associated with greatest amounts of ribose. Readings are obtained both for the standards and samples in a spectrophotometer at 660 mμ, the wave length of maximum absorption for orcinol.

The amount of RNA is proportional to the amount of ribose contained within it; thus this ribose determination is an indirect indicator of the amounts of RNA.

Diphenylamine Test (DNA)

Like the orcinol test, this reaction is a colorimetric one with varying shades of blue resulting.

Assume that the DNA is in 1 N PCA and that small amounts of it are available. Specific amounts of thymus DNA are brought to a volume of 2.0 ml with 1 N PCA for a standard curve and 2.0 ml samples of DNA are used. 4.0 ml of diphenylamine reagent is added to standards and samples. This reagent consists of 1.5 gm of diphenylamine in 100 ml of glacial acetic acid plus 1.5 ml of concentrated sulfuric acid. 0.1 ml of aqueous acetaldehyde is added for every 20 ml of the reagent. The acetaldehyde increases the sensitivity of the test. The color is developed by incubating at room temperature for sixteen to twenty hours. Readings for each standard and sample are obtained at 595 mμ in a spectrophotometer. The standard curve is determined and amounts of DNA in each sample are extrapolated from the curve.

ANALYSIS OF BASE COMPOSITION

There are a number of procedures to identify qualitatively and quantitatively the nucleic acid bases, nucleosides or nucleotides. The first two procedures, paper chromatography and electrophoresis, require that the DNA or RNA be hydrolyzed and then placed on filter paper. Column chromatography can be used with both DNA and RNA in hydrolyzed or intact form. The last two procedures, density gradient estimation and thermal denaturation, are useful only with DNA.

Paper Chromatography

The nucleic acid sample is hydrolyzed by 88 per cent formic acid or 70 per cent PCA (DNA) or 1 N HCl (RNA) at 100°C for one hour. The bases from RNA can be easily separated but the bases from DNA require the stronger acidic treatment before they are isolated. However, the purines of both DNA and RNA are easily extracted. It is the pyrimidines of DNA which are resistant to quick extraction.

Following hydrolysis, the acid fluid is evaporated and several drops of distilled water or dilute HCl added to dissolve the bases. A drop of the solution is then placed on Whatman #1 filter paper and two-dimensional chromatography is performed. (See Appendix A.) The first dimension solvent is methanol-concentrated HCl-distilled water and the paper is maintained in the chromato-cab for eight to ten hours. The second dimension solvent is isopropanol-ammonium hydroxide-distilled water; the paper is removed after twelve to sixteen hours.

The spots corresponding to the bases are located by ultraviolet light, marked and cut out. An extra spot as control is also cut. Each spot is minced finely and placed in a centrifuge tube with 5 ml of 0.1 N HCl. The tube is shaken and incubated overnight at 37°C. During this interval it is advisable to shake well a number of times. The tube is then centrifuged, the fluid is obtained, and its absorbancy spectrum determined by a spectrophotometer.

Each base has a characteristic curve. For example, in 0.1 N HCl the maximum absorption occurs as follows: A — 262 mμ; G — 248 mμ; U — 260 mμ; C — 278 mμ; and T — 265 mμ. The nucleotides and nucleosides of each base have maximum absorbance at about the same point as the base.

Even though a number of the nucleic acid constituents have a maximum at approximately the same point, they are easily distinguished by the overall characteristics of the curve, including the maximum and minimum points.

The molar concentration of each base is proportional to its absorbance and can be determined by a formula which is discussed in detail by Beaven, Holiday and Johnson (1955). The most appropriate procedure is to obtain the absorbances for varying amounts of each of the bases and then to estimate the amount of the unknowns from these curves. From the molar concentration of each base the molar percentage or proportion follows easily. An interesting phenomenon in this context is the hyperchromic effect, i.e., the absorbance of an intact nucleic acid is about 30 per cent less than the sum of the absorbance of the four bases which comprise it.

Electrophoresis

The bases, nucleosides or nucleotides are obtained by hydrolysis and placed on filter paper as indicated in the above section. The paper is placed in an electrophoretic apparatus in which electrical current is imposed. In a medium which will conduct electricity the constituents will move at different rates. (See Appendix A.) For example, in 0.05 M ammonium formate buffer at pH 3.5, the nucleotides of the four bases will move as follows (cm/2 hr at 20v/cm) : cytidylic acid, 6.5; adenylic acid, 8; guanylic acid, 14; and uridylic acid, 16 (Smith, 1955) .

The spots are located by ultraviolet light, the constituents eluted, and the quantity estimated by absorbency as indicated in the above section.

An alternative means of estimating the amount of each constituent with electrophoresis and paper chromatography which precludes eluting is to stain the paper with a suitable chemical to locate the components. The paper is then scanned optically and a densitometer trace or curve can be provided. The amount of the component is proportional to the area in the curve.

Column Chromatography

In this procedure the hydrolyzed sample is adsorbed on suitable material and the bases, nucleosides or nucleotides are eluted one by one by increasing the amounts of the eluting chemical. For example, the hydrolyzed bases of RNA are dissolved in a small amount of 2 N HCl and poured into a Dowex-50 column. A solution of 2 N HCl is then added at a rate of 0.6 ml/min. and the bases will elute one by one. U will be completely removed by approximately 75 ml; C by 125 ml; G, by 290 ml; and A, by 650 ml. The greatest amounts of each of the four will be eluted as follows: U — 50 ml; C — 100 ml; G — 200 ml; and A — 525 ml.

Each of the four fractions would be obtained in a number of tubes and the amounts of each determined by absorbancy curves.

The methylated albumin column discussed in Appendix A is able to separate intact DNA and RNA of varying base composition by passing through the column a series of buffered saline solutions of increasing salt concentration.

Density Gradient Estimation

Schildkraut, Marmur and Doty (1962) have found that the base composition of DNA can be determined from its buoyant density using a cesium chloride density gradient centrifugation procedure. They have developed a regression equation relating buoyant density to the proportion of G-C pairs in DNA from a comprehensive study with fifty-one different DNA samples ranging from man to the viruses. The G-C composition estimated by this procedure for fifty-one DNA samples was consistent with that obtained by other procedures.

The basis for the relationship between buoyant density and G-C content is found in the G-C pairing which has three hydrogen bonds whereas the A-T pair has only two, Thus, the buoyant density of DNA sample increases directly with increasing amounts of G-C. The regression equation of Schildkraut *et al.* is:

$$\text{buoyant density} = 1.660 + 0.098 \text{ (proportion of G-C)}$$

One ml of the DNA sample in saline-citrate solution is placed in a centrifuge tube with 4 ml of cesium chloride of such density that the buoyant density of the overall solution will be 1.700 g cm^{-3} (determined by a refractometer). During centrifugation, more dense cesium chloride particles and other materials will reach an equilibrium point below the center of the tube; less dense particles will settle above the center; and materials of 1.700 g cm^{-3} density will band at the center of the tube. For example, the buoyant density of DNA of rat liver is 1.699 g cm^{-3} (Schildkraut, Marmur and Doty, 1962), and this DNA would reach an equilibrium state near the center of the tube. From the above equation the proportion of G-C would be .40.

The solution of cesium chloride with the DNA sample is centrifuged at 44,770 rpm in a Spinco Model L Preparative Ultra Centrifuge for twenty hours, at which time an equilibrium state is attained. The solution is then run through a density gradient fractionator with an attached ultraviolet densitometer.

The presence of the DNA is indicated by a curve which is traced by the densitometer. Drops of fluid will be collected at the peak of the curves representing DNA. The refractive index is determined by a refractometer and the buoyant density computed from this index by the following equation:

buoyant density $= 10.8601$ x refractive index-13.4974 (at $25°C$)

Then the G-C proportion is available by substituting in the regression equation. As soon as one ascertains the G-C proportion, the A-T proportion is automatically determined. For example, if the buoyant density of a DNA sample were 1.689, the proportion of G-C would be .30. Therefore, inasmuch as the amounts of A and G are equal to T and C, respectively, the relative proportions of the four bases would be: A, .35; T, .35; G, .15; C, .15.

A major advantage of this procedure is that the buoyant density of amounts of DNA as small as one microgram can be determined and the overall procedure is quick.

Thermal Denaturation

Like the buoyant density procedure, this technique uses a physical property of DNA which is influenced by the G-C pairing. Marmur and Doty (1962) discovered that if DNA is heated, the double stranded molecule is denatured and split into single stranded ones. The transition from the double strand to the single strand state begins at different temperatures for DNA molecules with varying amounts of G-C pairs. As the amount of G-C increases, higher temperatures are required to denature the DNA. They have reported with 41 DNA samples that if the midpoint of the transition from double strand to single strand state is employed, the following relation holds:

thermal denaturation midpoint $(T_m) = 69.3 + 0.41$
(percentage of G-C)

This procedure involves using a small amount of DNA in a saline-citrate solution. The solution is placed in a DK-2A Ratio Recording Beckman Spectrophotometer and the solution is slowly heated. After an allowance of ten minutes at each temperature for equilibrium to be attained, an absorbance curve is obtained.

However, only the absorbance at 260 mμ (the wavelength of maximum absorbance for DNA) is used for estimation of T_m. When the two stranded molecule begins to split, a sharp increase in absorbance occurs. When denaturation is complete, absorbance reaches a maximum and further increases in temperature do not change the absorbance. The temperature which corresponds to the midpoint of the absorbance change during the transition is used in the above equation.

Marmur and Doty (1962) report that the thermal denaturation midpoint for rat liver is 86.5°C. The percentage of G-C would be 42 per cent. These results are close to those obtained with density gradient estimation and by other procedures.

Analysis of Other Structures

The analytic procedures of the previous section were concerned with primary and/or secondary structure. Tertiary and quaternary structure are, obviously, of great importance. However, at this time little is known concerning these aspects. Two main approaches have been utilized to ascertain these structures, as well as secondary structure. These are x-ray diffraction and electron microscopy.

X-ray Diffraction

This procedure is one that greatly aided Watson and Crick in formulating the model of DNA. The procedure has been restricted almost entirely to crystalline substances, or at least to highly ordered samples such as oriented fibers (Luzzati, 1963). An x-ray beam is scattered by electrons in the atomic nuclei of the sample. Since the electrons are clustered around the atomic nuclei, the scattering centers can be taken as atoms, and an atomic scattering factor calculated. With the wavelength of 0.5 to 2.0 Å commonly used, individual atoms can be resolved because the shortest interatomic distance is close to 1 Å. This ability to locate atoms is the basic feature of x-ray diffraction procedures.

Electron Microscopy

An electron microscope operates in principle like the light microscope except that it uses high speed electrons instead of light waves. The electrons are focused by magnets; the image can be seen on a fluorescent screen or can be photographed. An electron micrograph (photograph) is similar to an x-ray photograph because the beam of electrons in the microscope must pass through the subject before reaching the photographic plate.

For better resolution, after placing the sample on the electron grid, a thin film of metal such as uranium or platinum is sprayed onto the sample from one side. The area containing the spray is not affected by the electrons; they are scattered by the coat of metal and do not reach the photographic plate. In this manner one gets effective contrast between the sample and background; the length and shape of the shadow reveal the height and surface irregularities of the specimen. Specimens can be enlarged 100,000 or more times. This procedure has been useful in observing chromosomal and DNA structures (Beer, 1961).

In recent years electron microscopy has been combined with autoradiography (see Appendix A) to determine exact points in the cell where nucleic acid synthesis is occurring.

INDEX